C000245540

The Wild Geese of the Newgrounds

The Whitefronts arrive with a Lesser Whitefronted Goose

The Wild Geese of the Newgrounds

Paul Walkden

Illustrations by Peter Scott

"There is a peculiar aura that surrounds in my mind anything and everything to do with wild geese. That I am not alone in this strange madness, I am sure; indeed, it is a catching complaint, and I hardly know any who have been able to resist its ravages when once they have been exposed to infection."

From '*Morning Flight*' by Peter Scott. Published by Country Life, 1935.

Friends of WWT Slimbridge

First published 2009

Published by the Friends of WWT Slimbridge
The Newgrounds,
Slimbridge,
Gloucestershire
GL2 7BT

isbn : 978-0-9561070-0-8

The Wild Geese
of the Newgrounds

Design & Layout by
Lazarus Press
Unit 7 Caddsdown Business Park
Bideford, Devon EX39 3DX
www.lazaruspress.com

Printed & Bound by
R Booth Print
Penryn
Cornwall
TR10 8AA

Contents

Foreword

Lady Scott,
Honorary Director WWT

Paul Walkden has lived in the vicinity of the Wildfowl & Wetlands Trust for over 30 years and through his interest in wild geese and wildlife art he came to know my husband, Peter Scott, very well. He has now been inspired to make an intensive study of the history of the Severn Estuary and in particular of the Newgrounds at Slimbridge.

The White-fronted Geese have the most beautiful call of all the grey geese and Paul has obviously been captivated by their magic. As his special love, he has been able to include a mass of information about them covering a long period together with well researched historical information about the area.

His record keeping has been meticulous and I am so glad he has felt able to share all this information with us in this excellent book.

Philippa Scott

Whitefronts taking off. Peter Scott

Sir Peter Scott

Acknowledgements

Thanks must first go first to Lady Scott who answered so many questions and requests. Her knowledge, interest and enthusiasm for the project helped immensely. It was also to my great pleasure that she allowed me to use Peter Scott's artwork and illustrations which adjoin and enhance the text and finally she kindly took the time to write a foreword.

Bettie Sloane bears special mention as she read the drafts, correcting my grammar, spelling and in making so many useful comments including the suggestion of adding the chapter on Ringing and Goose Netting. I surely could not have done it without her help, encouragement and support. Also to Bettie's brother John Sloane who besides being a great supporter of WWT made suggestions and coaxed me into producing this for the centenary of Peter Scott's birth.

To Clive my son I thank him for helping me get my head round computers; he also organised some scanning and designed the dust wrapper. His fiancée Lizz also helped with suggestions and layout; their constant support is very much appreciated.

Martin McGill (goose fiend) who helped with chapter four and also made other helpful suggestions. To David Chaffe I offer my thanks for friendship and in helping me understand the daunting task of producing a book, besides his many other suggestions, especially pushing me into getting the job done.

For work in scanning the artwork and illustrations I thank Ian and Tracey Davie and also for an enjoyable day in the heart of Snowdonia. Bob Radford helped put my lists of dates into the graphs that look so much better; so to him my thanks.

To my family; Sue, Clive and Sarah I offer my love and thanks for their support and time in allowing me to disappear for hours on end, be it weekends when I should have been home, or holidays when they wished we were doing something that they considered sane. They don't understand my passion for geese; however they did allow me time to bring this exciting project to fruition.

I am indebted to The Friends of Slimbridge who decided to publish this book in celebration of the centenary of Peter Scott's birth. The Chairman of Friends, Graham Maples, supported and helped with photographs. All proceeds will be for the benefit of the Slimbridge WWT centre.

I would like to dedicate this book to the late Sir Peter Scott and Lady Scott (Phil) with whom I had/have the pleasure of knowing and working over a number of years. My admiration of them knows no bounds. Also to fellow goose watchers, some of whom I have known over 30 years: Pete Alder, Joe Blossom, Richard Chappell, John Dryden, John Garner, Rick Goater, Haydn Jones, James Lees, Graham Maples, Brenda & John Moatt, Martin McGill, Mike Ounstead, Dave Paynter, Theo Rhys-Jones, Mike Robinson, Jeremy Squire, Neil Smart, Bettie Sloane, Chris Temblett and Clive Walkden.

Paul Walkden

Introduction

It is late September when the excitement rises; it is only a matter of days now before the geese begin to arrive on the Newgrounds at Slimbridge. Geese have a special something that is hard to explain. It might be that they congregate in massive numbers, cover vast distances on migration, pair for life, are site loyal or that there is likely to be something exciting mixed in with them. Whatever it is they are special.

The White-fronted Geese continue to decline in numbers here on the Severn. However their numbers overall are thankfully stable. It seems the feeding grounds of Holland have a greater pull. Or could it be global warming? Some notes and an entry from my 1982 diary: 'In the Berkeley Vale in January we have over 12" of snow, it is the most snow in living memory. It is cold and remained so into February. Sunday 21st February, off early to the Trust in search of geese, what a magnificent day of viewing, 4,500 Whitefronts, 3 Lesser Whitefronts, a Greater Snow Goose (finally found), 21 Bean, 12 Pinkfeet, 2 Barnacles and 2 Brent. With the feral Greylag and Canada Geese, that's a full house'. What a magnificent day that turned out to be, watchers today I feel will never be lucky enough to see that again at the Newgrounds, Slimbridge.'

This book is an insight into the geese of the Severn Estuary and that special place, the Newgrounds of Slimbridge, where Peter Scott founded the Severn Wildfowl Trust in 1946. I have lived close to the River Severn at Berkeley, some five miles down-river from the Newgrounds at Slimbridge for some thirty-seven years. I, however, arrived in Gloucestershire in 1972 with a mind to meet Peter Scott, who was my childhood hero, but also to be near the Trust, so I could observe the ducks and geese that I had heard so much about in his magical television and radio programmes. I feel very privileged to have known Peter Scott, to have sat and talked with him in his studio, to have counted ducks from the studio tower hide with him and to have bird-watched with him. He truly was a remarkable man. It was Sir David Attenborough, another great conservationist, who named Peter as "the Patron Saint of Conservation".

It was Peter himself unknowingly that named this book, in an early diary of his from the time of the Trust's formation. Detailed in his own handwriting, he describes in great detail, the goose numbers, arrival dates of the geese, the build up of the geese, different species of geese mixed in with the Whitefronts, other bird sightings, his rocket netting trials and trips catching geese and general diary notes.

A number of friends having seen this small tome have asked why the Newgrounds is spelt as one word; well in a nutshell it is the way Peter wrote it on the cover of this early diary. His father, Captain Robert Falcon Scott of Antarctic fame also kept meticulous diaries and in one of his very last letters whilst he lay stranded with his colleagues in the Antarctic wrote to his wife Kathleen, "Make the boy interested in natural history if you can. It is better than games. They teach it in some schools". Kathleen Scott, Peter's mother, certainly succeeded in this. She, also a diarist, was a fine sculptor who studied under Rodin in Paris. Her exceptional works include the bronze statue of her husband, Captain Robert Falcon Scott, which stands in Waterloo Place, London.

Peter Scott, Father of Conservation

Chronological listing

Prepared by Paul Walkden

1909: Born 14th September, at 174 Buckingham Palace Road, London. The family home demolished to make way for the Greenline coach station.

1911: Father Captain Robert Falcon Scott leaves for the Antarctic. ('Terra Nova' expedition 1910 - 1912) (Previous 'Discovery' expedition 1901-04)

1912: Father Captain Robert Falcon Scott and his comrades (Wilson, Evans, Oates & Bowers) reach the South Pole (17th January) and tragically all die (29/30th March) on the return journey.

1917: Mother takes job in Paris so she moves there with Peter.

1918: Went to West Downs Preparatory School in Winchester. (to 1923)

1922: Mother Kathleen Scott marries Edward Hilton Young. (Later Lord Kennet of the Dene)

1923: Goes to Oundle School near Peterborough. (to 1927)
Wayland is born. (half brother).

1924: First illustrations published in '*Everday Doings of Insects*' by Evelyn Cheeseman.

1925: Birdwatching forays to the River Nene floods between Aldwincle and Lilford. First Grey Geese found, 200 mainly European Whitefronts with family parties of Pinkfeet.

1926: Illustrates '*Adventures among Birds*' by three schoolboys, privately printed. Family move to 100 Bayswater Road, Leinster Corner.

1927: Leaves school and goes to Trinity College, Cambridge to read Natural Science. (to 1930).

1928: Shoots his first goose on the Wash at Terrington. It was Peter's wildfowling forays that gave him his fascination with wildfowl and ultimately gave us the greatest conservationist of our time.

1929: First articles written for Country Life magazine. '*Wild Geese*' 24 August issue and '*Wild Geese and Ducks*' 30 November issue, both were illustrated by his paintings.

1930: Peter gains his degree in the history of art and architecture.

1931: Studies at the Munich Academy for a term.
Joins the Royal Academy School as a pupil. 15th December. (to 1933).

1932: Wins pair-skating championships at Westminster ice rink.
Goes to live at Borough Fen Decoy.

1933: First exhibition of paintings held at Ackermann's Gallery, London.
Moves into the East Lighthouse at Sutton Bridge where the Nene runs into the Wash.
Two paintings accepted by the Royal Academy for the Summer Exhibition.

1934: First short story published, '*Mr Spriggs and the Crane*' in the Cornhill Magazine. October.

1935: Book '*Morning Flight*' published by Country Life.

1936: Visits Hungary as special correspondent for 'The Field' magazine.
Represents Great Britain in single-handed sailing in the Olympic Games at Kiel. Wins a bronze medal.
Illustrates his step-father's book, '*A Bird in the Bush*'.
First broadcast for the BBC a 15 minute talk on dinghy racing.

1937: Wins the Prince of Wales cup for International 14' dinghies for the first time in Lowestoft.
Visits Persia and the Caspian Sea in search of Red-breasted Geese.

1938: Wins the Prince of Wales cup for International 14' dinghies, Falmouth.
Designs trapeze wire to support a crew member outboard. It was then banned but re-instated some 30 years later.
Book '*Wild Chorus*' published by Country Life.
Exhibition in Arthur Harlow's Gallery in New York. Did a series of five etchings.

1939: At the outbreak of war volunteers for the Royal Naval Volunteer Reserve.
Visits Northern Ireland to check on theory of another race of White-fronted Goose.

1940: Joins *HMS Broke,* appointed First Lieutenant.
Invents camouflage scheme for ships in HM Navy.

1941: Promoted to First Lieutenant of a destroyer in World War II.
Mentioned in despatches for his efforts in the rescue of the crew of *HMS Comorin*. Flies with the R A F on two bombing raids over Germany.

1942: Marries Elizabeth Jane Howard, 28th April.
Awarded the MBE (for inventing the night camouflage scheme for ships in World War II).
Mentioned in despatches for his part in the Dieppe Raid.
Appointed Lieutenant Commander.

1943: Daughter Nicola born.
Becomes senior officer of a flotilla of Steam Gun-boats in World War II.
Awarded the Distinguished Service Cross for his gallantry in a raid into the Baie de le Seine.
Mentioned in despatches for his part in a Cherbourg raid.
Wins a bar to his DSC for gallantry in a channel action.

1944: Joins planning staff of Coastal Command to prepare for D-Day.

1945: Appointed to command a new frigate, *HMS Cardigan Bay*.
Book '*Battle of the Narrow Seas*' published.
Resigns from the Royal Navy to stand as Conservative Candidate for Wembley North.
First post-war exhibition at Ackermann's Gallery.

1946: Wins the Prince of Wales Cup for International 14' dinghies. Brixham.
Founds the Severn Wildfowl Trust. Inaugurated 10th November.
Becomes joint presenter of Children's Hour radio programme, 'Nature Parliament'.

1947: Mother Kathleen dies of leukaemia aged sixty-eight.
Employs Philippa Talbot-Ponsonby as his secretary.
Trust membership reaches 1,000.
One of the commentators to the Royal Wedding.

1948: Describes the Greenland White-fronted Goose *Anser albifrons flavirostris* as a new sub-species with Christopher Dalgety.
First testing of rocket nets for the capture of wild geese.
First Bewick's Swan drops in to the pen of Whistling Swans at Slimbridge.
Caught for the collection and named Mrs Noah.

1949: Expedition to the Perry River region, Canada.
HRH Princess Elizabeth's first visit to Slimbridge.
Book '*Portrait Drawings*' published.
Book '*A key to Wildfowl of the World*' first published in Second Annual Report.
Mother's memoirs published, '*Self Portrait of an Artist*'.

1950: Two Hawaiian Geese arrive at Slimbridge for captive breeding programme.

1951: Marries Philippa Talbot-Ponsonby in Rejkjavik, Iceland.
Expedition to the Hofsjokul ice cap in the central highlands of Iceland to study Pink-footed Geese. Ringed 1100 Pink-footed Geese.
Book '*Wild Geese and Eskimos*' published.

1952: Daughter Dafila born June.
First Hawaiian Geese breed at Slimbridge.

1953: Awarded CBE for work connected to the Wildfowl Trust.
Further expedition to Iceland, rings over 9,000 Pink-footed Geese.
Television programme begins, forerunner to Look. (See 1955).
Book '*A Thousand Geese*' published.
Becomes Vice-president of the International Union for the Conservation of Nature. (IUCN)
Peter's first public lecture; 'Wild Goose Chase' and presents his colour film; 'Pursuit of Pinkfeet'. Royal Festival Hall, 13 January.
New house built with studio at Slimbridge to Peter's design.

1954: Son Falcon born.
Breaks the sailing speed record at Cowes.

1955: Severn Wildfowl Trust becomes The Wildfowl Trust.
Presenter of new television programme Look 14th June. (Runs until 1970)

1956: Report, '*The Geography, Birds and Mammals of the Perry River Region*' with Harold C Hanson and Paul Queneau published.
Takes up the sport of gliding.
On the suggestion of Konrad Lorenze snorkels on the Great Barrier Reef introducing him to the world of coral fish. Becomes one of his great passions.

1957: Book '*A Coloured Key to the Wildfowl of the World*' published. Still in print 2006.
Book '*Wildfowl of the British Isles*' with Hugh Boyd published.
The Wildfowl Trust's second centre at Peakirk in Cambridgeshire opens to the public.

1958: Completes his Gold C for Glider flight. Only the thirty-fourth time issued to a British Pilot. (the flight requirements are 5,000 mt height, 500 km distance & 300 km distance with declared landing site).

1959: Visits the Galapagos Isles to help found the Charles Darwin Foundation.
Whilst there makes film for the BBC.

1960: Elected Rector of Aberdeen University by the student body.
Book '*Faraway Look One*' with Philippa Scott published.
Book '*Faraway Look Two*' with Philippa Scott published.
Invited HRH The Prince Philip, Duke of Edinburgh, to be President of The Wildfowl Trust. 1960-65 (and again in 1972-79).

1961: Co-founder of the World Wildlife Fund, set up to raise funds. Designs its Panda logo and becomes first Chairman.
Invites HRH The Prince Philip, Duke of Edinburgh, to be the first President of the World Wildlife Fund.
Autobiography published, '*Eye of the Wind*'.

1962: Book '*Animals in Africa*' with Philippa Scott published.
Originator of the Red Data Books for WWF, identifying endangered species.
Becomes Chairman of Survival Service Commission of the IUCN.
First 30 Slimbridge-reared Hawaiian Geese released in Hawaii.
Appointed Admiral of the Manx fishing fleet.

1963: Wins the British Gliding Championship.

1964: Selected as helmsman of Sovereign for the America's Cup, Newport, Rhode Island. Comes second.
Society of Wildlife Artists formed. Peter becomes first President. (until 1974).
Becomes a grandfather. Nicola's first born, Daniel.

1965: Edits first Annual report of World Wildlife Fund, '*The Launching of a New Ark*'.

1966: Visits the Antarctic to make film for the BBC.

1967: Land purchased at Welney in Cambridgeshire and reserve established.

1968: First of twenty-six cruises as guest lecturer for the Eric Linblad cruises.

1969: To the Danube Delta in Romania in search of the Red-breasted Geese.

1970: Booklet '*The Wild Swans at Slimbridge*' with Phillipa Scott published.
Wildfowl Trust Centre in Welney, Cambridgeshire opens to the public.

1971: Wildfowl Trust Centre in Caerlaverock near Dumfries opens to the public.
Becomes Director of Survival Anglia and starts his commentaries on their wildlife films.
Story '*The Pond*' published in *The Twelfth Man,* an anthology put together for HRH The Prince Philip, Duke of Edinburgh.

1972: Book '*The Swans*' with Wildfowl Trust published.

1973: Awarded the first Knighthood for conservation.
Writes the conservation plan for Mauritius.
Book '*Waterfowl*' published.

1974: Appointed Chancellor of the University of Birmingham by the senate, served ten years.

1975: Wildfowl Trust Centre in Martin Mere, Lancashire opens to the public.
Wildfowl Trust Centre in Washington near Newcastle-upon-Tyne opens to the public.

1976: Wildfowl Trust Centre in Arundel, Sussex opens to the public.

1977: Receives the United Nations International Pahlavi Environment Prize along with Jacques Cousteau. Each receives $25,000.

1978: Travels to Siberia in search of the breeding grounds of the Bewick's Swans.

1979: Co-founds the Falkland Islands Foundation.

1980: Book '*Observations of Wildlife*' published.
Awarded Master Wildlife Artist by Leigh Yawkey Woodson Art Museum, Wausau, Wisconsin.

1981: Awarded the IUCN John Phillips Medal and the WWF Twentieth Anniversary Special Award.

1982: International Whaling Commission agrees to phase in a moratorium on whaling.

1983: Book *'Travel Diaries of a Naturalist 1'* published.

1984: Suffers a mild heart attack whilst at home.

1985: Book *'Travel Diaries of a Naturalist 2'* published.

1986: Awarded the J P Getty prize of $50,000.
WWF awards its Gold Medal at its twenty-fifth anniversary celebrations.
Party at Slimbridge to celebrate the Trust's fortieth birthday.

1987: Appointed a Companion of Honour by Her Majesty the Queen. (Limited to 65 people).
Made a Fellow of the Royal Society. Both in June.
Book *'Travel Diaries of a Naturalist 3'* published.

1988: A coral fish, *cirrilabrus scottorum,* named after Peter and Philippa Scott.

1989: Peter's sixteenth exhibition held at Ackermann's Gallery in London. Opened by Prince Philip.
The Wildfowl Trust changes its name to The Wildfowl & Wetlands Trust.
Retrospective exhibition of Peter's work put together by Cheltenham Art Gallery, publishes book *'Sir Peter Scott at 80'* as exhibition catalogue.
Exhibition travels round the UK.
Taken ill at home and dies in Bristol hospital, 29th August, a fortnight short of his eightieth birthday.
Memorial service to celebrate his life, St Paul's Cathedral, London. 20th November.
Memorial service to celebrate his life, the Church of St John, Slimbridge. 30th November.

1990: Wildfowl & Wetlands Centre at Castle Espie on Strangford Lough opens to the public.

1991: Wildfowl & Wetlands centre in Llanelli, South Wales opens to the public.

1992: *'The Art of Peter Scott, Images from a Lifetime'* published by Sinclair-Stevenson. Selected and with captions by Lady Scott.

2000: Wildfowl & Wetlands Trust London Wetland centre at Barn Elms opens to the public.

2009: Centenary of his birth celebrated.

Whitefronts on the Tack Piece

Chapter 1

Peter Scott and The Wildfowl & Wetlands Trust

"The marshes will be filled with their unparalleled music as they flight at dawn and at dusk. When the moon is full they will pass unseen in the steel-grey sky to their feeding grounds, but their cry will echo across the flat fields. Like a symphony of Beethoven, the call of the geese is everlasting, and those who have once known and loved it can never tire of hearing it."

Peter Scott. *Morning Flight.* Country Life. 1935

Peter Scott kept a collection of wildfowl in enclosures at the East Lighthouse at Sutton Bridge, where the River Nene runs into the mighty Wash Estuary. He moved into the East Lighthouse in 1933, when he was 24 years old, and made this his home for five years. He had been mulling over plans for an organisation dedicated to the scientific study and the conservation of wildfowl for some time. However, the Second World War intervened.

Peter went into the Royal Naval Volunteer Reserve and became First Lieutenant of the destroyer *HMS Broke* in 1941. In 1942 he designed the night camouflage scheme taken up by the Royal Navy for which he was awarded an MBE. He later in 1943 became Senior Officer commanding a flotilla of steam gunboats (his own named *Grey Goose*) and saw much action, winning the

Distinguished Service Cross with Bar and was mentioned in dispatches three times. In 1945 he was appointed to command a frigate.

Following the end of WWII Peter began looking for the ideal site from which to launch his planned organisation. The East Lighthouse was no longer on the foreshore, as a sea wall had been built to reclaim land for agricultural use. Crops were grown to help feed the booming post-war population of Britain. This meant his old home, some half a mile from the sea, had lost its appeal. He had previously considered four sites: Brogden in Kent, Amberley Wildbrooks in Sussex, High Halstow in Kent and Slimbridge in Gloucestershire. However, an extraordinary incident that occurred in 1943 decided which of these sites would become Peter's base. Will Tinsley, a Lincolnshire farmer and close friend of Peter's had a wild Lesser White-fronted Goose drop into his collection of tame wildfowl. Peter theorised that if Lesser White-fronted Geese were to be found in Britain, it was most likely that they would occur within large cohorts of European White-fronted Geese, the major flocks of which wintered on the Newgrounds at Slimbridge, twelve miles south of Gloucester aside the Severn Estuary. The Berkeley family owned these Severn lands.

Peter had been to the Severn Vale twice previously, in September 1928, too early to see geese and again in 1937 at the invitation of the then owner of the Berkeley estate Captain R.G. Berkeley. The Berkeley estate once covered a huge area, some 44,500 acres. The family held manorial rights over the foreshore and to the centre of the Severn. They preserved this site for goose shooting parties, organised annually. However, numbers of birds shot were relatively small and disturbance was kept to a minimum. These lands included two cottages and the remains of a duck decoy, which historically had kept the Castle of Berkeley supplied with ducks for feasting, the surplus being sent to London markets for sale.

The Cottage, c.1946

Peter had the opportunity to put his theory to the test on a December day in 1945. He and several friends, John Winter, Clive Wilson and Howard Davis headed toward the River Severn from the village of Slimbridge, went over the Gloucester-Sharpness canal, down a muddy track and arrived at a wartime pillbox overlooking the river. On scanning the flocks of geese congregated on lush grasslands bordering the Severn, known as the 'Dumbles', they spotted first a young Bean Goose, then a Barnacle, a Brent, and a Greylag. There were also Pinkfeet, all of them mixed in with the flock of two thousand wild European White-fronted Geese. Alas, no sign of the Lesser Whitefront. The following day they returned to the same pillbox and within 30 minutes had found a Lesser Whitefront, distinguished from the European Whitefront by the small pink bill and yellow eye ring, smaller size and quicker feeding pattern. Peter noted in his autobiography *The Eye of the Wind* this special moment, "My spine tingled delightfully as it does in the slow movement of Sibelius's Violin Concerto. Here almost too easily was a vindication of my far-fetched theory. It was, no doubt, a small recondite discovery, a minor ornithological technicality, yet for me it was a moment of unforgettable exultation - a major triumph, an epoch-making occurrence, a turning point; or is it only in looking back on it that I have invested it with so much significance because, in the event, it changed the course of my life?" Later in the afternoon they moved further down the marsh and found yet another Lesser Whitefront. Peter had noted that the black bars on the bellies of the geese were all different and so easily told apart. On that momentous day they had recorded the third and fourth sightings in Britain of the Lesser White-fronted Goose. This was surely the place for his planned organisation.

Discussions followed and arrangements were made to lease an area from Captain R. G. Berkeley. Pens were built for the wildfowl. Along with the four wartime pillboxes, which were ideal for watching geese from, a new hide was erected in the summer of 1946. On Sunday 10th November 1946 at the Patch Guest House (now apartments) by the aforementioned canal bridge a resolution was signed bringing the Severn Wildfowl Trust into

being. Later 'Severn' was dropped from the title and in 1989, in recognition of the increasing involvement in wetland habitats, it became The Wildfowl & Wetlands Trust.

The Wildfowl & Wetlands Trust has truly become an international force in the field of conservation, particularly in the breeding of rare and threatened wildfowl species. It has an international reputation in the scientific study of waterfowl and wetlands and is an educator for people from all walks of life, young and old. Recreation is also an important part of the Trust's ethos, with thousands of visitors flocking every year to its centres. It now has nine centres of excellence at various sites across the United Kingdom. These centres are based at Arundel in West Sussex, Caerlaverock in Dumfriesshire, Castle Espie in Northern Ireland, Llanelli in South Wales, Martin Mere in Lancashire, Slimbridge in Gloucestershire, Washington in Tyne and Wear, Welney in Cambridgeshire and the Wetland Centre in London. (See appendix for full details of centre addresses.) Most contain collections of wildfowl from all over the world and all centres offer fine bird watching facilities. Some in fact offer unrivalled viewing of one of the great wildlife spectacles in Britain, a skein of geese in flight. To see geese in their thousands is something that is hard to express with mere words, but their movements are poetry in motion and the noise never fails to stir excitement beyond description. The Trust can offer this experience with European White-fronted Geese at Slimbridge, Brent Geese at Strangford Lough, Northern Ireland, Pink-footed Geese at Martin Mere, Lancashire and the Barnacle Geese on Solway Firth, Scotland.

A Picture of Geese by Peter Scott
(poem written pre-war)

When the moon is clear and full in the sky,
And the wild geese come in from the sand,
And the tide whispers up and the curlews cry -
Then I think that I understand.

Is it only for worms that the curlews call
'Cur-lee' as they go to feed?
But how can I understand at all
If worms are all they need?

Is it only potatoes on cold black earth
That the geese are looking for;
Or for grass at the edge of a northern firth
Where the sea comes in with a roar?

But it's life to a man who can understand
And it shall be life to me:
And then, when the geese come in from the sand,
Through me all men shall see.

Chapter 2

The River Severn

"The whole scene is dominated by the silver snake of the river winding down past Gloucester and into the Bristol Channel. My home lies opposite that indefinable part of the estuary which is not quite river, nor quite sea. From the house, at the times of Spring tide, we can hear the flood as it rushes in over the sand on its way into the funnel-mouth of the river which will turn into the bore. Over our sands the little wave is only a foot high at most, but up in the narrows round the great bend it will gradually build up into a breaking roller more than six feet high."

Peter Scott in his Foreword to *The Severn Bore* by F W Rowbotham.
David & Charles, 1964

The River Severn is Britain's longest river, originating high on the Plynlimon Hills of Mid Wales. On its majestic journey of almost 220 miles it drains seven English counties and half of Wales, drawing water from some 4,300 square miles. It claims the second highest tidal rise in the world. The lowest point of the Severn is between Beachley and Aust; here the difference between low and high water is 14.5 metres. This amount of water being forced into the funnel shaped estuary creates a fast moving mountain of water. As this tidal force speeds upriver both narrowing banks and a shallower channel restrict it. Once it has passed the horseshoe bend of Arlingham, further tightening of the strait causes the tide to rise up on itself, creating a wall of water, which on the highest tides can be 2 metres. This is the world famous Severn Bore.

The Severn's highest tides and bores coincide with the full moon, as when the sun and moon lie directly in line with the Earth they create the greatest gravitational pull. These bores are advertised widely, with hundreds and occasionally thousands of people turning up to watch the spectacle. The narrow village lanes of Stonebench, a favourite spot to watch from, become grid-locked city-style. Frequently the bore waters break the banks and much comic misery follows with flooded cars and very wet watchers. However, most spectators will testify that it's worth it, the wait full of anticipation, the low rumbling heard as the bore nears, which grows to a sound likened to an approaching diesel train before the waters finally arrive, crashing at the banks, throwing spray and debris everywhere. Then onward it goes, speeding towards Gloucester, leaving ever-rising waters in its wake and often cheering folk.

The Severn Estuary, one of the biggest in Britain, is shaped by a number of large rivers flowing into it. These include the Wye, Parrett, Avon, Usk and the Severn itself. This vast area of water and our generally mild winter climate make it an exceptionally important wintering site for thousands of migratory birds, especially the wildfowl, (swans, geese, ducks) and waders. Due to the importance of this area for these migratory birds the upper Severn has been a Site of Special Scientific Interest for a number of years. It was designated a RAMSAR site in 1988, the following year becoming a Special Protection Area. The lower estuary followed soon after.

The name Severn is derived from the Welsh name Habren, which became Hafren and was translated into English as Sabren. It was changed to Sabrina and finally to Severn. The Legend of Habren is as follows: King Locrine of Loegria was betrothed to a girl by the name of Gwendoline. Prior to this marriage the King took a fair German maiden, Estrildis, hostage. Falling in love he abandoned Gwendoline. In a distressed state Gwendoline went to her father who forced the King to marry her. However, Locrine kept his mistress hidden in his castle and visited her nightly. Estrildis became pregnant and gave birth to the King's daughter whom she named Habren. Soon after, Gwendoline's father died and King Locrine discarded Gwendoline and placed Estrildis on the throne. Gwendoline fled to her brother who raised an army and besieged the King's castle at Dolforwyn, Abermule in

Mid Wales. During the battle mother and daughter, Estrildis and Habren, were seized and thrown into the River Severn, where both were drowned.

The best area on the Severn for wildfowl is known as the 'Newgrounds', (refers to the area within the sea wall), which is almost 3 miles long on the Eastern bank of the Severn close to the village of Slimbridge. It covers 1200 acres and has been so called since circa 1637. In around 1550 the Severn channel settled down for a long period toward its Forest of Dean shore. The result was a large movement of mud and sand to the opposite side creating the Newgrounds. The drier and stable part of the Newgrounds is known as the Warth and the moving silts that come and go with the tide as the Dumballs or Tumps. The name Dumballs persisted for over 350 years and is now called the Dumbles. This land is excellent pasture and was traditionally used for summer grazing of cattle, for the resting of working farm horses and care of mares with foals. The Severn at this point is a mile across, giving ample area for roosting wildfowl.

The village of Slimbridge (previously known as Slymbridge, Saxton's map 1577) lies at the heart of the beautiful low-lying Severn Vale, locally known as The Berkeley Vale, which runs almost from Gloucester to Bristol and is bordered by the Severn and the Cotswold escarpment. The high tides of the Severn often ran up as far as the church in Slimbridge prior to the sea wall construction. A number of these sea walls have been constructed and parts of the original earth wall can still be seen in the grounds. The Berkeley Vale pasture is of exceptional quality and ideal for dairy cattle. It has its own breed, The Gloucester, which produces rich milk, which was used mainly for cheese production. The best milk created the Double Berkeley cheese, lower-grade milk was used for Single Berkeley. As the cheese was extensively exported the name was changed to the now well-known Single or Double Gloucester.

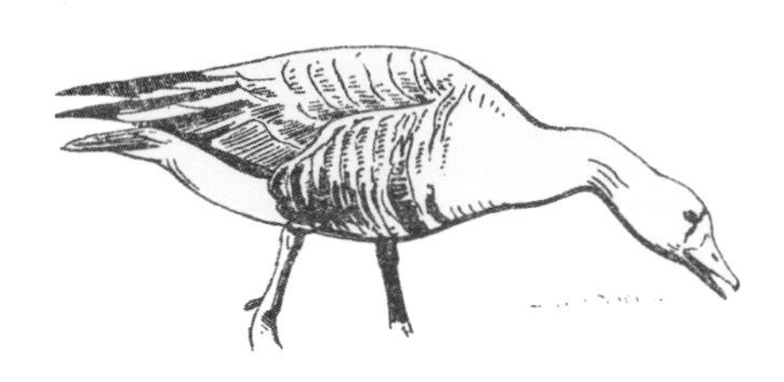

The Second World War agricultural department earmarked 400 acres of the Newgrounds in 1941 and later increased this to 550 acres. The claimed land included fields that had been heavily grazed by geese and considered severely damaged. The main crops grown for the war effort were potatoes and wheat. Both the winter and spring wheat grown gave exceptional harvests. In 1943 some 380 acres of potatoes were grown. The problem of harvesting this bumper crop was left to 300 local schoolgirls and their teachers. A tented village was set up and an Italian chef from the Savoy Hotel, London catered for them. They certainly worked well sending off some 50 tons a day. On one record day 115 tons were lifted and dispatched. Her Majesty, Queen Mary, took an interest and visited the camp on several occasions.

One day whilst I was watching the geese with Peter Scott in a hide overlooking the field called the Tack Piece he outlined what an exceptional field it was. He went on to tell me that during the War Agricultural Tenure, this very field had yielded the greatest crop of wheat in Gloucestershire for a number of years. Peter believed this to be due to the geese and duck grazing that occurred and the natural fertilizer they left behind. He was always amazed at the sheer numbers of wildfowl that feed in this one field and often referred to it as an avian Serengeti. The number of geese feeding in a field and the duration of time feeding in them is known at the WWT as goose days.

The numbers of wild birds using our estuaries in the U.K. are regularly recorded. These counts of birds are completed monthly on all estuaries and other wetland areas, around 2000 sites altogether. It is a joint scheme of The Wildfowl & Wetlands Trust, The British Trust for Ornithology, The Royal Society for the Protection of Birds and The Joint Nature Conservation Committee. The work is undertaken by a volunteer network, managed by The Wetland Bird

Survey (WeBS), which is based at the BTO, (British Trust for Ornithology). The aims of this scheme are to identify population sizes, determine trend in numbers and distribution, and to recognize important sites for water birds. Depending on the number of a species present, a number is given to mark the importance of the site. There are two categories, International or National.

The Severn is of international importance for The Bewick's Swan, Pintail, Shelduck, Dunlin, Redshank, Lesser Black-backed Gull and of national importance for Wigeon, Gadwall, Teal, Shoveler, Mallard, Pochard, Tufted Duck, Water Rail, Moorhen, Grey Plover, Lapwing, Snipe, Black-tailed Godwit, Curlew and Ringed Plover on passage. This makes the Severn one of the top ten estuarine sites in this country. These sites, that are so important for our wetland birds, are often seen as wastelands. However, estuarine mud is rich in plant and invertebrate life, which in turn feeds the visiting over-wintering birds. In fact estuaries are more productive than the very best agricultural land.

White-fronted Geese

Peter Scott.

Chapter 3

The White-fronted Goose

"Their skeins were just as beautiful across the dawn sky, their wild music just as evocative, their long migrations just as mysterious. So many things were still unknown about these wonderful birds, and I wanted to find out more."

Peter Scott in his Foreword in *Wild Geese of the World* by Myrfyn Owen. Batsford. 1980.

There are two species of White-fronted Goose in Europe: the Greenland Whitefront (*Anser flavirostris*) that breeds in west Greenland and over-winters in Ireland, Scotland and west Wales, and the European or Russian Whitefront (*Anser albifrons*) that breeds throughout northern Siberia, east of the Kanin Peninsula and over-winters in north-west Europe, the Mediterranean, Caspian Sea and Persian Gulf, eastern China and Japan. It is estimated that there are 20,000 Greenland Whitefronts currently wintering in Great Britain and almost 4,000 European Whitefronts.

The European Whitefront is a small grey goose, which has a brown body, orange legs and pink bill. The bill is of medium size, with a band of white feathers to its base, hence the name. Its underside has black bars that are variable in size; some birds appear to have a wholly black underside. Juveniles in early winter have no black belly bars and no band of white feathers; however, as the winter progresses the white front feathers appear and a few black flecks become visible on their bellies.

The Greenland Whitefront is very similar but is a darker bird with an orange bill. All geese tend to be vocal and the Whitefront is no exception; their call is often described as hysterical laughter.

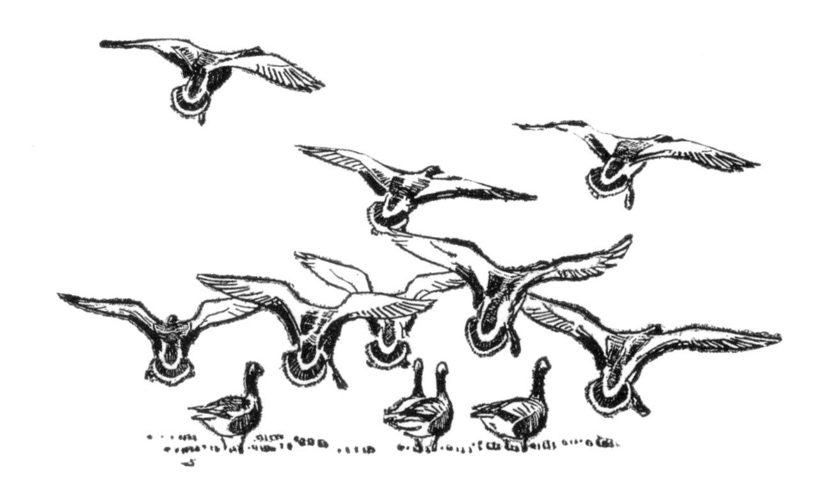

It is very musical, high pitched and noted in early works as pleasurable.

The Newgrounds on the Severn remains the most important wintering site within the U.K. for the European Whitefront. The Wetland Bird Survey lists the other sites: the Swale Estuary (2nd), Heighham Holmes (3rd), North Norfolk Coast, North Warren and Thorpeness Mere, Alde Complex, Dungeness Pits, Walland Marsh, Minsmere Levels, Lower Derwent Valley, Middle Yare Marshes, Breydon Water and Berney Marshes, Thames Estuary and the Crouch-Roach Estuaries. These are all sites of national importance.

In the early sixties the three most important sites were the Severn, Dryslwyn in Dyfed, which held a maximum of 1500 and the Hampshire Avon that held up to 2,000 geese. Prior to the sixties the Towy valley in Carmarthenshire was an important site where Whitefronts were first recorded in 1949 when 600 were discovered. Bridgewater Bay was the most important site in Somerset where 500 were regular, with a maximum count of 1,500 recorded. In Wales the Dovey Estuary recorded up to 500 birds, and regular records came from the Dee Estuary as well as floodwater around Denbigh and St Asaph in North Wales, the latter geese from the Mersey Estuary where up to 1,100 birds were recorded. The continuing downward trend of numbers of the European Whitefront in the United Kingdom means its future appears uncertain. However, internationally they are doing very well. There is no doubt that there is a natural shift in their wintering distribution.

The Greenland Whitefront is another story. The United Kingdom is its main wintering area. All the important sites are in Scotland, the most important being Islay holding around 13,000 birds. Dr John Berry writing in the *International Wildfowl Enquiry, Volume 2, The status and distribution of Wild Geese and Wild Duck in Scotland,* published by the Cambridge University Press in 1939 states: "Islay seems always to have been the most important wintering ground of the White-fronted Goose in Scotland. The species was already plentiful there in 1871 ... and by 1892 Islay was quoted as undoubtedly its headquarters for the whole country". When writing this no one was aware that this was not the European Whitefront. The Greenland Whitefront at this time was unknown to science. It was in 1948 that Peter Scott and Christopher Dalgety separated this species from the European species. But for the war (1939-45) their research would have been completed earlier. It was published in the bulletin of the British Ornithologists' Club (Volume 68. No.6., May 7th 1948.) It seems quite extraordinary that these sub-species had remained undiscovered for 180 years, as Scopoli first described the European Whitefront as early as 1769.

Geese have few natural enemies. Peregrine Falcons have been noted to harass geese on the Newgrounds, but have never been seen to strike a goose and foxes are unlikely to take a healthy bird. The geese on their constant feeding pattern may appear relaxed, but the opposite is true. If you watch any goose flock, there is always a number of birds with their heads up, watching for danger. The geese are very wary and are alert at all times.

Human disturbance can be problematic to the geese. Careless people wandering into the reserve area have all the geese airborne and clamouring to get as far away as possible from the threat. Fortunately this does not happen too often; signs are posted on the boundaries warning people not to enter.

Fog creates a real problem for geese; they seem to fly blind in thick fog. The birds fly and call amidst the fog and can get totally disorientated and lost. It is not uncommon following fog for a number of birds to be lost. It can take some days and in some cases weeks to get numbers back up to full strength. At these times it is not unusual to have reports of geese heard and seen miles inland.

Another problem is prolonged hard weather, when the ground is frozen for long periods or snow-covered. Being grazers geese need grass available all the time. If it is not available they are forced to move in search of open areas. Up and down the river they fly, looking for grass that has been uncovered by the waters of the incoming and outgoing tides. When we have these bouts of hard weather I hear the geese flying up and down the river into the night, constantly calling. It's a harrowing time for the geese, which always causes me concern. I cannot settle and lie awake listening and feeling at a loss for the poor birds. During prolonged hard weather the geese will feed in tussocky or rougher grassland.

Aircraft are also a major problem to geese. However since the early days of the Trust the Newgrounds area has been a no-fly zone. Peter Scott worked tirelessly to achieve this, keeping meticulous records whenever an incident occurred. The early Trust annual reports give much information on this problem. Today's problems tend to be microlite aircraft, air balloons and helicopters that often follow the course of the river. Many more hobby flyers are around these days especially at weekends and have a greater ignorance of the no-fly zones over the Trust areas.

The Grey Geese

Chapter 4

Other Wild Goose Species at WWT, Slimbridge

"As birds go, they are rather intelligent. They make long and still incompletely understood migrations, they fly in skeins at dawn and dusk, calling most tunefully, and often they gather in vast aggregations which constitute, in many countries, the finest wildlife spectacle still to be seen. All of these give the Wild Geese and Wild Swans a special magic in the hearts and minds of most people who have come to know them well over a long period of time."

Peter Scott writing on geese. *Observations of Wildlife*. Phaidon Press. 1980

All wild geese species are gregarious and travel long distances on their migrations. It is not unusual for geese to get mixed in with the wrong flocks as one skein passes another heading in a different direction. As a consequence each and every year a good number of other goose species finds its way to the Newgrounds at Slimbridge mixed in with the Whitefront flocks. On the whole these stray geese appear in groups and family parties. Occasionally singles are spotted. It is these other species that make goose watching so interesting and special. As mentioned earlier, the very reason why Peter Scott came to the Newgrounds was the hope of finding that special visitor 'The Lesser White-fronted Goose'.

Wild geese are referred to as either 'grey' (*Anser*) or 'black' (*Branta*) geese. The 'grey' geese are the Pinkfoot, Whitefront, Lesser Whitefront, Bean and Greylag. The 'black' geese are the Barnacle, Brent and Canada.

The Lesser White-fronted Goose (*Anser erythropus*)

This special little grey goose has become a very scarce visitor. From the early days of the Trust this goose was generally recorded each year. The Lesser White-fronted Goose was visiting every year through the 1940s and 50s, with a surprising six, possibly eight birds in the period of January to March 1956. Throughout the 1960s, 70s and 80s odd birds would appear, sometimes two in each year as in 1969, 1977, 1980, 1982, 1983 and three in 1975. In the 90s birds continued to get scarcer. A neck collared bird arrived on 9th December 1990 staying through into March. It returned in 1992 again staying on until March. The next bird was recorded on 26th January 1995 staying through until February 26th. One bird arrived on January 5th remaining until March 24th. Another arrived on February 4th 1998 departing on February 27th. The last recorded bird was in 2003 arriving in February.

The Pink-footed Goose (*Anser brachyrhynchus*)

Records of the Pink-footed Geese on the Newgrounds were not kept until the early thirties. In 1933 their numbers hit 1250 and stayed level in 1934, when 1250 birds also visited. In 1935 they dipped to 550, in 1937 rose to 1050 and in 1938 dropped again to 650. By 1941 they were down to 55, experienced an increase in 1943 to 110 and 105 in 1944 and in 1945 fell once more to 80. When Peter Scott arrived at the Newgrounds, accurate and more detailed records were kept. It was now recognised that the Pink-footed Geese arrived first around the last week in September. Peak counts were during November. From 1946 until the 1960s numbers varied from as low as 58 in 1948 to a maximum of 136 in 1957. Numbers would quickly drop as birds moved off, presumably further north. Most years a number of Pinkfeet were found with the flock of Whitefronts. In recent years it has been more common to find odd birds or small groups. However, 30 were counted on January 18th 1979 and flocks of 52 recorded in December 1984 and again in 1999.

The Greylag Goose (*Anser anser*)

The Western Greylag is a native goose, however most records on the Newgrounds are of re-established stock. A number of these birds were introduced to Frampton Court Estate in the mid fifties as a joint venture between this local estate and the Wildfowl & Wetlands Trust. Peter Scott believed that the birds would move to the Trust enclosures, making a spectacular sight for visitors. He was proved correct. Therefore records of wild birds at the WWT are always suspicious. However, Trust staff

know when true wild birds are about, as they behave quite differently. Early records at the Trust outline odd birds mixed in with the flocks of Whitefronts, prior to re-established birds being released into the area. A much rarer find is the Eastern Greylag (*Anser rubrirostris*). Martin McGill found two on 26th February 2006 at Slimbridge. Next day they had moved to the Frampton marsh, where I was lucky enough to catch up with them. Previously another find was one on 2nd/3rd March 1968 by D I M (Ian) Wallace. Current mid winter counts of Western Greylag vary from 4-500 birds.

The Bean Goose (*Anser fabalis*)

This goose species, which is the rarest of the 'grey' geese, puts in an appearance most years. Singles or pairs and up to six or seven birds would be the normal expectation. However, a maximum count of twenty-eight was made on December 13th 1987, which was quite exciting if not exceptional. There are two sub species, the Taiga or Western Bean Goose (*Anser fabalis fabalis*) and Tundra or Russian Bean Goose (*Anser fabalis rossicus*) both of which occur, occasionally in the same year. However, the Tundra Bean is by far the most common.

The Barnacle Goose (*Branta leucopsis*)

These beautiful geese are seen most years. However, definite records are difficult to keep as the Trust had for many years a free flying flock of some 200 birds. This was part of a long-term scientific study of the species founded by Dr Myrfyn Owen, a scientist who headed the research department at the Trust before being made Director

General. Over time the numbers of birds thinned out. A re-established flock of around 120 has built up since the early nineties and remains in the area flying to and from the gravel pits at Frampton. Wild birds found at Slimbridge have been noted to have been from the Spitsbergen flock as well as the Greenland flock over the years.

The Brent Goose (*Branta bernicla*)

A welcome visitor that turns up most years in small numbers. The maximum number was a count of 70 birds flying upriver on 23rd March 1996. Other notable numbers include 16 that arrived on 23rd January 1991, 31 in early February 1991 and a flock of 67 on the ebb tide on 10th March 2000. Previous to that 16 arrived on 23rd January 1991. Two sub-species occur in Europe: the Dark-bellied Brent and the Light-bellied Brent. By far the most common to turn up on the Newgrounds is the Dark-bellied Brent (*Branta bernicla bernicla*) which occur around the south, south east and south west coasts of Britain. The rarer species for the Newgrounds is the Light-bellied variety (*Branta bernicla hrota*) as they over-winter predominantly on Strangford Lough in Northern Ireland. Peter Scott's first record was in September 1946. The last record was a bird in 1997 staying until 19th January 1998. On December 20th 1989 a Black Brant (*Branta bernicla nigricans*), a more unusual visitor from the Americas, was recorded by Pete Alder. Thoughts and discussions continue on the possibility of the Grey-bellied Brent goose. An adult showing these characteristics was found on the Dumbles on 2nd November 2001 by Brenda Moatt.

The Canada Goose. (*Branta canadensis*)

At Slimbridge, mirroring the trend elsewhere in England, this bird's numbers continue to increase. The Frampton Court estate close to the Newgrounds introduced a naturalized flock on their gravel pits in June 1953. A number of estates introduced these geese onto lakes for both aesthetic and sporting purposes. This flock spends increasingly more time within the collection at Slimbridge or on the Newgrounds. Current winter counts vary between 400 - 550.

Red-breasted Goose (*Branta ruficollis*)

The first record of a Red-breasted Goose on the Newgrounds at Slimbridge occurred in February 1941. The second, and a first for the Trust, was a juvenile bird arriving on 8th until 25th January and again from 13th February to 5th March 1954, only the eleventh recorded in Britain. On 23rd December 1953 it was documented in the *Gloucestershire Bird Report* that a Redbreast was shot on Hasfield Ham, near Gloucester. The next visit for Slimbridge was a bird arriving on January 24th staying until March 13th in 1959. A wait of four years ensued before the next bird arrived on December 31st in 1963 staying until March 8th. Two birds arrived in 1967: a juvenile arrived on January 5th, which stayed until 15th, then an adult arrived February 4th staying until 28th. In 1969 one bird arrived on January 19th and stayed until 31st. The last Red-breasted Goose on the Newgrounds was recorded on 17th January staying until March 1st, 1984.

The Snow Goose (*Anser caerulescens*)

A rare vagrant but well documented, three adults reported in the winter of 1890, then three adults with five juveniles arrived in October 1901, then three adults in November 1906 and again another three birds in the winter of 1916/17. One of these birds was shot and considered to be Lesser Snow Goose. Interesting that records were consistently of three birds, could any of these sightings have been the same birds? More recently on 15th December 1981 an adult Greater Snow Goose put in an appearance on the Newgrounds and remained with the flock of Whitefronts until February 20th 1982. It was suggested at one point that this may have been an escapee from a collection. However, its behaviour was very much that of a wild bird. Visitors came from far and wide to see it.

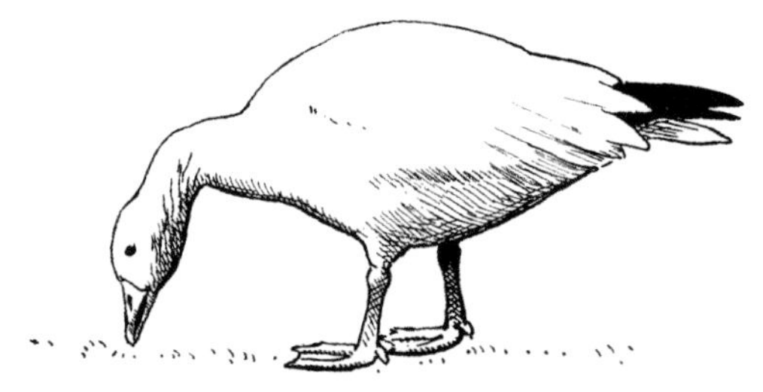

Greater Snow Goose

Chapter 5

The Ringing of Geese and Rocket Netting

"As I came to the net I made a quick count, thirty-two geese. We had succeeded. We had made the first great catch of geese alive for ringing. It was a satisfying moment."

Peter Scott in *'The Eye of the Wind'*. Hodder & Stoughton. 1961.

The Severn Wildfowl Trust was founded with four aims: scientific study, education, recreation and conservation. These aims remain true to this day. Scientific study includes bird ringing (banding in America) and has been an important part of the Trust's work. A small lightweight ring with a unique number is placed on the bird's leg. The aim is to determine migration routes, wintering and breeding distribution and how long birds live, relying on recovery of the dead bird or a retrap (re-capture), thus providing subsequent information.

Geese have always been trapped and hunted by man as a food source. Trapping today however is generally carried out to ring the bird for scientific study.

Peter Scott developed rocket netting for the catching of wild geese in Britain in 1948. Some hundreds of hours were spent on trials with rockets and propellants. The army and the Schermuly brothers (who developed the rocket pistol and flares for saving life at sea) were drafted in to help. Nets with various mesh sizes were tried before the ideal size was found. Spring arm traps had been tried initially but without success.

A successful catch. Peter extricating Pinks in Scotland.

A Barnacle Goose round-up, Spitsbergen, 1970s.

Two nets generally facing each other were rocket propelled over the top of the feeding geese that have wandered into the catching area once the trap has been set. Each net is 60 yards long by 20 yards deep and made of 1" mesh. Around the edge of the net are net flaps to contain the geese once the net has been fired, to stop them clambering out and escaping. Six rockets were attached by wire traces to each net, the rockets were modified 25-pound artillery shells. The propellant used was cordite. The angle of the rockets was crucial at 45 degrees. They were electronically fired from a mobile hide. This hide was painted in a camouflaged pattern designed by Peter. The time spent in this hide waiting for the right moment to fire was considerable. (This mobile hide was once described as containing the largest collection of Peter Scott works in existence. Peter was an incessant doodler and drew on any surface available.)

A great deal of preparation was required. First one had to locate where the geese were feeding; watching was then crucial to determine which part of the field held the most geese, where were the heaviest concentrations. Having watched these feeding grounds for many hours, sometimes for a number of days, the decision was taken as to where the best field might be to set the nets. It was off to an early bed then, as next morning the team had to be up to lay the ambush. Nets were unfurled and carefully laid out; lines set and attached to rockets, which were then loaded, cables from the rockets were then laid out to the hide. The nets and cables then had to be camouflaged with grasses or straw depending on what field type they were in. Next the decoys had to be laid out; these were stuffed birds, in various positions, feeding with head down or in a head up position. Only seven or eight decoys were used, as they were expensive and fragile. The decoy layout was a very skilled job and generally only Peter undertook the task. Everything in the feeding area had to look natural; nothing must look suspicious to the geese. All this had to be done prior to first light. Everything had then to be double-checked. Then the wait, would the geese return? If they did, it would take time before the correct number of geese were in 'the catching area', no good making a catch of a few birds. All the time and effort put in, everyone hoped a reasonable number of geese would enter the catching area to make it all worthwhile. What tension! Everyone had to remain very still and quiet. As the geese left their overnight roosting areas they would be heard, first the quiet noise, then building as the geese lift and make their way out to the feeding fields. Soon they came into sight, great V-formations flying high. Then they come in, whiffling down, spinning and turning, dispelling air from the wings to lose height rapidly. The geese now in the field, caution, don't want to disturb the geese now, allow them to settle and to start feeding. Finally when it was thought that a good number of birds was in the catching area the button could be pressed, the rockets fired, the bang, the swoosh as the nets were lifted over the geese, the geese clambering and calling as the majority of the birds in the field leave. Wait for the smoke to clear, then the dash to get to the geese to determine how successful the catch had been and to start quickly extricating the geese from the nets.

The geese would then be weighed, aged, sexed and various measurements taken. The small alloy ring had also to be fitted correctly. All these details had to be written down carefully and recorded before each goose was placed in its own small sacking holding pen. On completion of all the geese having been processed they could be released together, thus ensuring that family groups and the flock remained together. All this took place in the winter months when temperatures could be well below zero. Peter and his team of supporters (all volunteers) made a considerable contribution to our knowledge of geese.

An early catch at Slimbridge was on 15th February 1948; the nets were set on the 100 acre field. Thirty Whitefronts and one Pinkfoot were caught. Later, on 27th February some 71

Whitefronts were caught on the Dumbles. Other trials and catches were made on local farms and on the Frampton marshes north of Slimbridge. These local trials were in preparation for major goose netting trips, arranged for Scotland, which Peter had carefully planned. In March of 1950 around the Solway Firth some thirty Greylag and seven Pinkfeet were caught. In October of the same year a catch of three hundred and seventy-eight Pinkfeet was ringed. Further favourable trips were made in 1951. Other successful trips also took place in Lincolnshire and Yorkshire. Further development continued to reduce the time it took for the nets' trajectory; black powder took over from cordite with further success.

From its development in 1948 until 1962 the Wildfowl Trust ringed over 14,000 geese in England. This number consisted of 11,820 Pink-footed Geese, 1,200 Canada Geese, 580 White-fronted Geese and 565 Greylag Geese. By 1981 this total had grown to 30,000. Pinkfeet ringed numbered 21,716. An outstanding achievement.

In 1951 Peter Scott, James Fisher, Philippa Talbot-Ponsonby (later Mrs Peter Scott) and Finnur Gudmundsson went on an Icelandic expedition, a journey to the heart of Iceland. No one knew at this time where the main breeding grounds of Pink-footed Geese were. Peter believed Iceland would be the site. He also hoped to find some of his previously ringed birds on this expedition. (At this time some 634 Pinkfeet had been ringed in England.) Breeding grounds of the Pink-footed Geese had been discovered in Spitsbergen in 1855, Greenland in 1891 and Iceland in 1929, but which one was the main site?

Wildfowl are unusual in that they moult very quickly. In so doing they have a flightless period in the latter part of the breeding season. In ducks the male bird takes on the dull plumage of the female giving him better camouflage during this flightless period. The term given to this plumage change in wildfowl is 'eclipse'.

The rounding up and catching of geese during their flightless moult period had taken place in Iceland since time immemorial in goose folds, horseshoe shaped compounds built of stones. Peter believed that he could also round the geese up and hopefully catch large numbers in the same way; this could be achieved by using netting to form large catching pens. The birds could then be rounded up and driven into them. On 25th July 1951 some 247 geese were ringed in one catch, 94 adults and 6 retraps plus two retraps of British ringed birds. During this trip the team caught and ringed 1,151 Pink-footed Geese.

In 1953 Peter returned to central Iceland with another team for a second scientific expedition with a view to spending three to four weeks catching geese during the flightless period. An outstanding success, during this trip some 9005 Pinkfeet were rounded up and ringed, of which 126 were re-captures.

The Trust also had success in rounding up Barnacle Geese on the Spitsbergen breeding grounds. Expeditions took place in 1974, 1977, 1978, 1981 and 1986. By the early eighties almost twenty-five percent of the Spitsbergen flock had been caught and ringed.

Chapter 6

Wildfowling

"Wildfowl have long been a symbol in the minds of men, of freedom and lonely places, of wildness and timidity, of the strangeness which Ibsen conjured up in 'the wild duck'. Other images abound: a 'wild goose chase' leads us into the unknown, the impenetrable beyond of Nature. It is proverbially unsuccessful except for the skilled wildfowler. Wildfowlers stand apart, a breed of men for whom the desolation of the marshes fulfils some inner longing to be part of a spiritual mystery. Even to the urbanite, wandering in the half-light beside an estuary during his holiday, something of the mystery is apparent in the chorus of the wild geese at dawn or dusk, flighting from nowhere to here, only to return to nowhere as the season passes."

Peter Scott in *Waterfowl*. Berkshire Printing Co. 1973.

Wild geese are renowned for being site loyal and the European Whitefront is no exception. However, they are unique amongst geese in that they normally roost and feed on the same site. Other goose species fly out of their roosting ground at first light to their feeding grounds, which may be miles inland, returning at dusk to their safe roosting sites. These are often far out on mudflats in the most inaccessible and remote areas away from man and disturbance. The fact that the geese on the Newgrounds stay put once they have arrived was the very reason the lords of Berkeley protected the geese and this special site. Sport was an integral part of the country gentleman's life. However, shooting was carefully monitored and took place infrequently, so as not to unduly disturb the flocks of geese.

Normal goose shooting takes place with the wildfowler trying to position him/herself under the flight line of birds as they leave or return to the roost. The Whitefront on the Newgrounds traditionally needed a different approach. The geese were disturbed at one end of the marsh, knowing that they would fly up the marsh over the guns that had been previously positioned behind specially built screens (butts). Once the geese had moved up the marsh and settled again they were again disturbed so that they would fly back down the marsh. Geese, however, are very quick to learn where danger resides and will fly very high to avoid the areas containing guns. Constant disturbance can and will lead to desertion of an area, be it feeding grounds or the roost. The lords of Berkeley were very careful as to how often they shot, so as not to lose the geese. During the winter months when the geese were present, disturbance at all times was kept to a minimum and woe-betide anyone who dared to wander onto the Newgrounds!

Shooting still takes place on the Severn Estuary and when it occurs on the foreshore it is called wildfowling. The Gloucestershire Wildfowlers' Association, founded in 1956, has a membership of about 120 members and is responsible for large areas of the foreshore on both sides of the river from Gloucester down as far as the old Severn road bridge at Aust. They have in 2003 made their first land purchase of land adjacent to the Severn near Newnam on Severn, some 50 acres, which is mainly marsh, but includes a pond and a copse. This purchase was made possible by a loan from the Wildlife Habitat Trust.

The national and international importance of the Severn to our migratory wildfowl is a responsibility wildfowlers take very seriously. They work with Natural England and other conservation organisations to ensure the continued upkeep of the Severn habitat, its wildfowl and other species; they monitor shooting and suppress any poaching or unsporting activity. The wildfowlers shoot to the north of the Slimbridge reserve, but have ties with

The Wildfowl & Wetlands Trust to minimise disturbance and problems. This group of wildfowlers has for 23 years run an annual identification course for its members, which takes place over five Sunday mornings at the Slimbridge centre. A member of the Slimbridge staff oversees an assessment on week five. The course aims to educate its members of the conservation values of wildfowl and the Severn as an important wetland wintering area. Its main emphasis is about the identification of European wildfowl, including birds in flight that are likely to be encountered in this country. All wildfowling members must pass the assessment before being accepted as full members.

The sport of wildfowling normally takes place at dawn or dusk in the winter months, the season being 1st September to 31st January with an extension to 20th February, when shooting below the high water mark. The principle is to position oneself under a flight line of ducks or geese within a maximum range of 45 yards, this being the maximum range of a standard 12-gauge shotgun. Movement of wildfowl is always greatest during hard weather, gales, snowstorms or fog. As a consequence wildfowling is a sport for the hardy, having to sit out without moving under extreme conditions, and is not for the faint hearted. Birds taken are very few and far between. (60% of visits whilst wildfowling see no return). Birds taken are always for the table of one of the shooting cohort. It was wildfowlers who pushed for the ban on sale of dead geese, to stop unscrupulous gunners shooting in excess and selling them on to make profit. Wildfowlers feel very strongly about their sport and what is an acceptable number of birds to take. Their interests are often confused with these unsporting types who take advantage of hard weather movements, a prime example of the minority spoiling the good name of the majority.

Wildfowling is an attempt to outwit the wildest of birds in their own habitat, the taking of a natural, sustainable harvest.

Geese that can be legally taken in season are Canada, Greylag, Pink-footed and the European White-fronted Geese. Duck include: Mallard, Pintail, Gadwall, Shoveler, Wigeon, Teal, Tufted, Pochard and Goldeneye.

In the U.K. there are around 200 Wildfowling Clubs, which are affiliated to the national representative body, The British Association for Shooting and Conservation (BASC). BASC was founded in 1908 as 'The Wildfowlers' Association of Great Britain and Ireland'. With a membership of 130,000 it represents all sporting shooting. Its members set up the Wildlife Habitat Trust in 1986, which operates as the UK's shooting conservation fund. It has supported more than 60 projects and its main intention is to acquire important habitat that can be managed for the benefit of wildlife and shooting in partnership. A number of these projects has involved the establishment of nature reserves, both local and national. These projects represent an investment in wildlife conservation by shooting interests of more than £1,400,000.

The Wildlife Habitat Trust's main source of funding is the production of a habitat stamp each year, which depicts a goose, duck or game-bird species. Members of BASC and others can purchase this stamp at £5 which can then be stuck on their membership card, showing their commitment to conservation. Other items are also produced incorporating the artwork. These include prints, badges, postcards, greetings cards and first day covers. Many key wildlife artists of the United Kingdom have designed stamps. They include: Terance James Bond, Keith Brockie, John Cox, Barry Van Dusen, Robert Gillmor, Tim Hayward, Ben Hoskyns, Terence Lambert, Rodger McPhail, Julian Novorol, Peter Partington, Bruce Pearson, Darren Rees, Chris Rose, Keith Shackleton, Michael Warren and Owen Williams. Owen Williams' stamp design of 2001 was 'Pochard on the Severn', with a backdrop of WWT at Slimbridge including the magnificent Sloane Tower standing in the background. The 2009 stamp design will feature European White-fronted Geese on the Dumbles at Slimbridge by artist Peter Partington.

Wild Geese by Patrick R. Chalmers

They're shy as the otter, they're sly as the fox,
They're worse to approach than the craftiest hind,
You may freeze on the foreshore or crouch on the rocks,
You may soak in the sea-fog or wait in the wind,
Though their magical music will give you no peace,
Yet your bag shall go empty, for aren't they wild geese?

Honk-honk, honk-honk, the distant voices clank in;
The wet retriever trembles at your knee;
For he hears the lone notes falling,
Where the long grey tides are crawling,
Through the shouting west wind's buffets or the dripping fog's chill blanket,
As the wild geese come shoreward from the sea!

You may stalk them at sundown, at dawning's first flame,
They've ears for the wariest, softest of treads,
And, stook-time or snow-time, the end is the same -
A picket gives warning and up go their heads:
Yes, your boots (wet as sponges in spite of their grease)
You may wear brown paper in chasing wild geese!

Yet still, honk-honk, the call of them shall call you,
Where shot shall shake the raindrops from his sides,
Though you catch the drifting clamour
Through the sleet squall's sting and hammer,
Still the flight shall work its magic and the breathless stalk enthral you,
When the grey geese come shoreward off the tides!

Published by Eyre and Spottiswoode 1931 in *Rhymes of Flood & Field*

Arrival Dates of Wild Geese at the Newgrounds

1844	10th Sept.	1886	17th Sept.	1928	12th Sept.	1970	29th Sept.
1845	11th Sept.	1887	12th Sept.	1929	12th Sept.	1971	5th Oct.
1846		1888	25th Sept.	1930	17th Sept.	1972	2nd Oct.
1847	11th Sept.	1889	28th Sept.	1931	23rd Sept.	1973	24th Sept.
1848		1890	22nd Sept.	1932	16th Sept.	1974	9th Oct.
1849		1891	13th Sept.	1933	2nd Sept.	1975	25th Oct.
1850		1892	13th Sept.	1934	15th Sept.	1976	23rd Sept.
1851		1893	9th Sept.	1935	21st Sept.	1977	24th Sept.
1852	14th Sept.	1894	22nd Sept.	1936	23rd Sept.	1978	11th Oct.
1853	21st Sept.	1895	12th Sept.	1937	11th Sept.	1979	4th Oct.
1854		1896	20th Sept.	1938	15th Sept.	1980	29th Sept.
1855	23rd Sept.	1897		1939	16th Sept.	1981	18th Oct.
1856	21st Sept.	1898	14th Sept.	1940	12th Sept.	1982	6th Oct.
1857		1899	18th Sept.	1941	29th Sept.	1983	24th Oct.
1858		1900	22nd Sept.	1942	18th Sept.	1984	25th Oct.
1859	21st Sept.	1901	20th Sept.	1943	26th Sept.	1985	29th Sept.
1860	17th Sept.	1902	17th Sept.	1944	18th Sept.	1986	13th Oct.
1861	15th Sept.	1903	11th Sept.	1945		1987	2nd Oct.
1862	17th Sept.	1904	20th Sept.	1946	21st Sept.	1988	13th Oct.
1863	14th Sept.	1905	18th Sept.	1947	24th Sept.	1989	17th Oct.
1864	20th Sept.	1906	20th Sept.	1948	21st Sept.	1990	14th Oct.
1865	27th Sept.	1907	2nd Oct.	1949	25th Sept.	1991	11th Oct.
1866	23rd Sept.	1908	18th Sept.	1950	23rd Sept.	1992	4th Oct.
1867	20th Sept.	1909	14th Sept.	1951	27th Sept.	1993	30th Sept.
1868	22nd Sept.	1910	17th Sept.	1952	20th Sept.	1994	17th Oct.
1869	17th Sept.	1911	14th Sept.	1953	20th Sept.	1995	12th Oct.
1870	14th Sept.	1912	10th Sept.	1954	19th Sept.	1996	22nd Sept.
1871	15th Sept.	1913	15th Sept.	1955	14th Sept.	1997	15th Oct.
1872	17th Sept.	1914	4th Sept.	1956	24th Sept.	1998	1st Oct.
1873	14th Sept.	1915	20th Sept.	1957	26th Sept.	1999	9th Oct.
1874	17th Sept.	1916	14th Sept.	1958	28th Sept.	2000	23rd Sept.
1875	15th Sept.	1917		1959	1st Oct.	2001	6th Oct.
1876	12th Sept.	1918		1960	27th Sept.	2002	28th Sept.
1877	19th Sept.	1919		1961	24th Sept.	2003	14th Oct.
1878	13th Sept.	1920		1962	18th Sept.	2004	9th Oct.
1879	15th Sept.	1921		1963	28th Sept.	2005	9th Oct.
1880	16th Sept.	1922		1964	1st Oct.	2006	11th Oct.
1881	15th Sept.	1923	9th Sept.	1965	28th Sept.	2007	8th Oct
1882	13th Sept.	1924	12th Sept.	1966	30th Sept.	2008	30th Oct
1883	21st Sept.	1925	15th Sept.	1967	18th Nov.		
1884	21st Sept.	1926	13th Sept.	1968	27th Oct.		
1885	23rd Sept.	1927	12th Sept.	1969	20th Oct.		

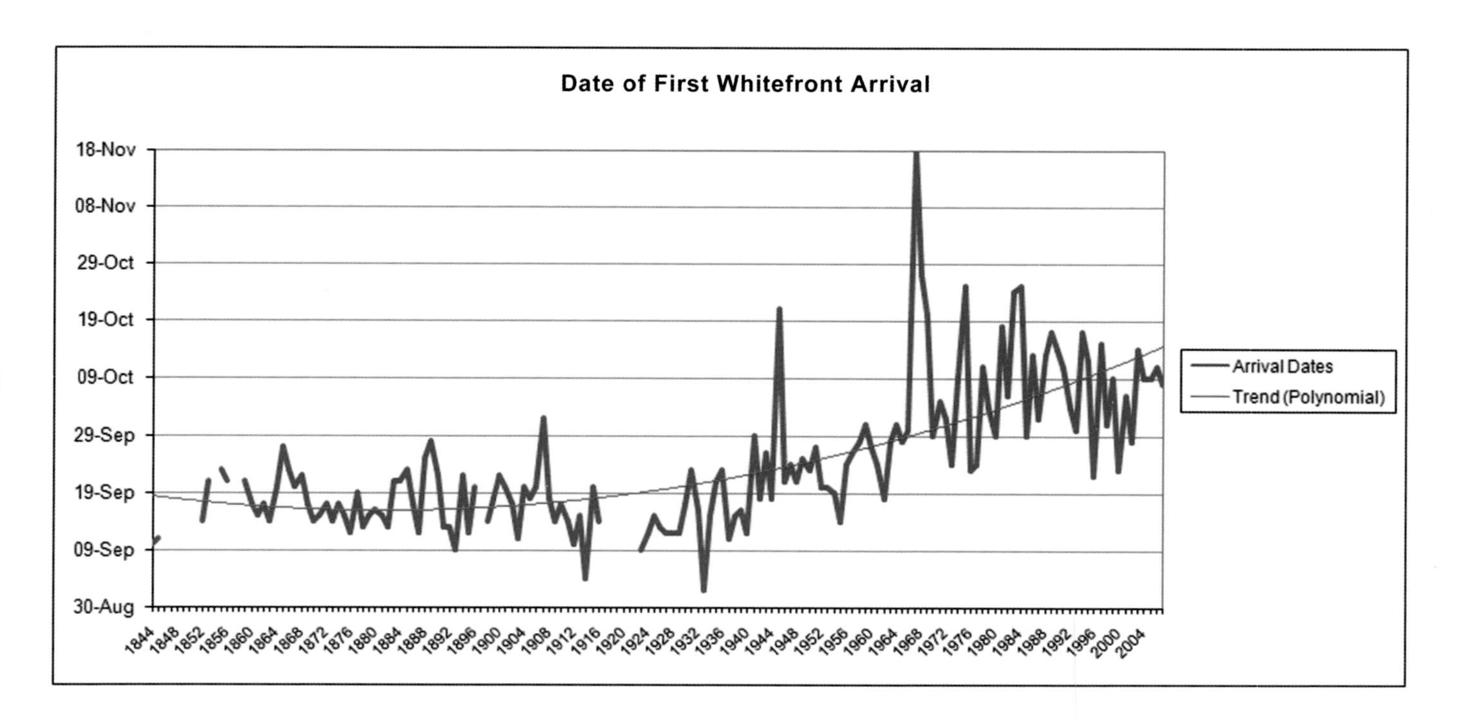

Date of First Whitefront Arrival
18-Nov
08-Nov
29-Oct
19-Oct
09-Oct
29-Sep
19-Sep
09-Sep
30-Aug
1844
1848
1852
1856
1860
1864
1868
1872
1876
1880
1884
1888
1892
1896
1900
1904
1908
1912
1916
1920
1924
1928
1932
1936
1940
1944
1948
1952
1956
1960
1964
1968
1972
1976
1980
1984
1988
1992
1996
2000
2004
Arrival Dates
Trend (Polynomial)

Maximum Counts of White-fronted Geese at the Newgrounds

Season	Count	Date
1946/47	4,200	11th Jan.
1947/48	3,000	26th Jan.
1948/49	3,800	15th Jan.
1949/50	3,500	27th Jan.
1950/51	3,700	29th Jan.
1951/52	2,500	16th Jan.
1952/53	4,700	8th Jan.
1953/54	5,000	23rd Feb.
1954/55	3,900	10th Feb.
1955/56	5,000	26th Feb.
1956/57	3,300	2nd Feb.
1957/58	4,200	16th Feb.
1958/59	5,000	14th Feb.
1959/60	4,200	21st Feb.
1960/61	3,500	22nd Feb.
1961/62	4,400	12th Feb.
1962/63	3,000	28th Feb.
1963/64	4,500	23rd Feb.
1964/65	3,150	25th Jan.
1965/66	5,500	9th Feb.
1966/67	4,200	18th Feb.
1967/68	6,700	17th Feb.
1968/69	6,600	29th Jan.
1969/70	7,600	26th Jan.
1970/71	6,000	18th Jan.
1971/72	3,350	9th Feb.
1972/73	6,000	15th Jan.
1973/74	4,500	20th Jan.
1974/75	1,450	17th Jan.
1975/76	2,800	18th Feb.
1976/77	3,600	26th Jan.
1977/78	2,600	4th Feb.
1978/79	5,100	11th Jan.
1979/80	2,100	15th Feb.
1980/81	3,000	11th Jan.
1981/82	4,500	10th Feb.
1982/83	3,040	3rd Feb.
1983/84	3,400	Mid Feb.
1984/85	4,200	13th Feb.
1985/86	4,300	16th Jan.
1986/87	3,500	25th Jan.
1987/88	4,607	26th Jan.
1988/89	3,770	19th Jan.
1989/90	3,200	Mid Jan.
1990/91	2,600	4th Feb.
1991/92	5,100	15th Feb.
1992/93	1,401	5th Feb.
1993/94	3,000	8th Feb.
1994/95	2,200	10th Jan.
1995/96	2,200	Mid Feb.
1996/97	2,780	16th Feb.
1997/98	2,501	20th Feb.
1998/99	1,840	30th Jan.
1999/00	1,931	23rd Jan.
2000/01	1,330	13th Jan.
2001/02	1,420	14th Feb.
2002/03	1250	14th Jan.
2003/04	800	17th Feb.
2004/05	745	7th Feb.
2005/06	788	4th Jan.
2006/07	542	23rd Jan.
2007/08	572	24th Jan.

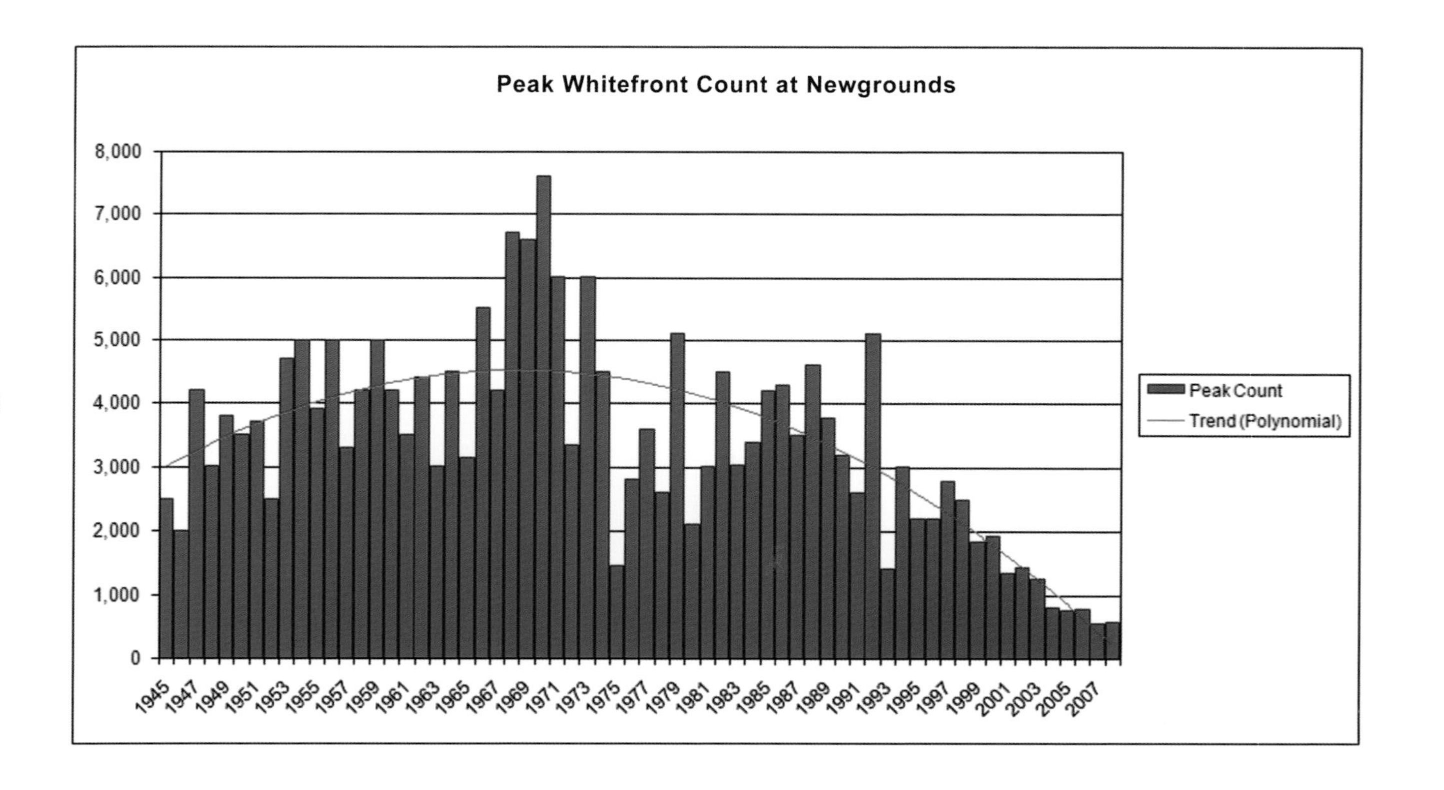
Peak Whitefront Count at Newgrounds
8,000
7,000
6,000
5,000
4,000
3,000
2,000
1,000
0
1945
1947
1949
1951
1953
1955
1957
1959
1961
1963
1965
1967
1969
1971
1973
1975
1977
1979
1981
1983
1985
1987
1989
1991
1993
1995
1997
1999
2001
2003
2005
2007
Peak Count
Trend (Polynomial)

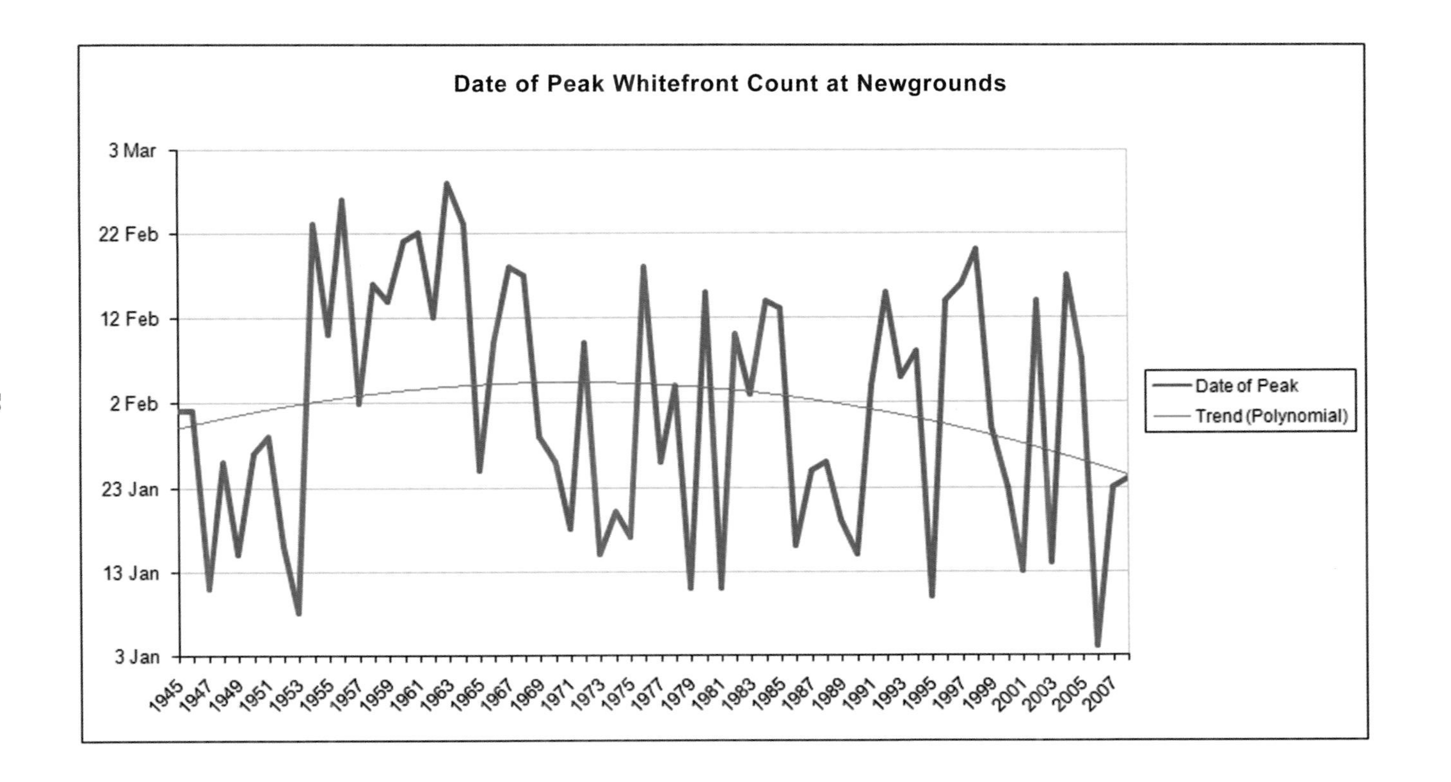
Date of Peak Whitefront Count at Newgrounds
3 Mar
22 Feb
12 Feb
2 Feb
23 Jan
13 Jan
3 Jan
1945
1947
1949
1951
1953
1955
1957
1959
1961
1963
1965
1967
1969
1971
1973
1975
1977
1979
1981
1983
1985
1987
1989
1991
1993
1995
1997
1999
2001
2003
2005
2007
Date of Peak
Trend (Polynomial)

Peak Counts of Pink-footed Geese at the Newgrounds

Year	No.	Date
1933	1250	
1934	1250	
1935	550	
1936		
1937	1050	
1938	650	
1939		
1940		
1941	55	
1942		
1943	110	
1944	105	
1945	80	
1946	95	10th Nov.
1947	120	6th Oct.
1948	58	30th Oct.
1949	62	16th Oct.
1950	63	1st Dec.
1951	117	26th Oct.
1952	73	30th Oct.
1953	103	4th Nov.
1954	120	6th Nov.
1955	94	25th Nov.
1956	65	11th Nov.
1957	136	1st Nov.
1958	61	31st Dec.
1959	45	3rd Jan.
1960	117	13th Nov.
1961	39	10th Dec.
1962	62	29th Nov.
1963	42	29th Sep.
1964	7	21st Sep.
1965	19	26th Sep.
1966	3	5th Mar.
1967	2	15th Jan.
1968	7	26th Jan.
1969	4	29th Dec.
1970	5	16th Jan.
1971	9	12th Jan.
1972	14	Mid Jan.
1973	2	20th Dec.
1974	2	1st Jan.
1975	6	21st Dec.
1976	2	1st Jan.
1977	1	1st Jan.
1978	5	5th Feb.
1979	30	18th Jan.
1980	5	21st Jan.
1981	5	29th Dec.
1982	12	Dec.
1983	1	28th Dec.
1984	52	28th Dec.
1985	1	29th Dec.
1986	2	20th Dec.
1987	11	1st Feb.
1988	2	23rd Dec.
1989	3	Mid Feb.
1990	2	9th Dec.
1991	9	18th Nov.
1992	8	Jan.
1993	18	Feb.
1994	14	16th Sep.
1995	12	Dec.
1996	12	24th Dec.
1997	8	Dec.
1998	13	20th Dec.
1999	55	28th Dec.
2000	11	13th Feb.
2001	10	9th Dec.
2002	3	27th Nov.
2003	4	4th Jan.
2004	0	
2005	1	6th Mar.
2006	2	1st Jan.
2007	3	26th Jan.
2008	1	1st Jan.

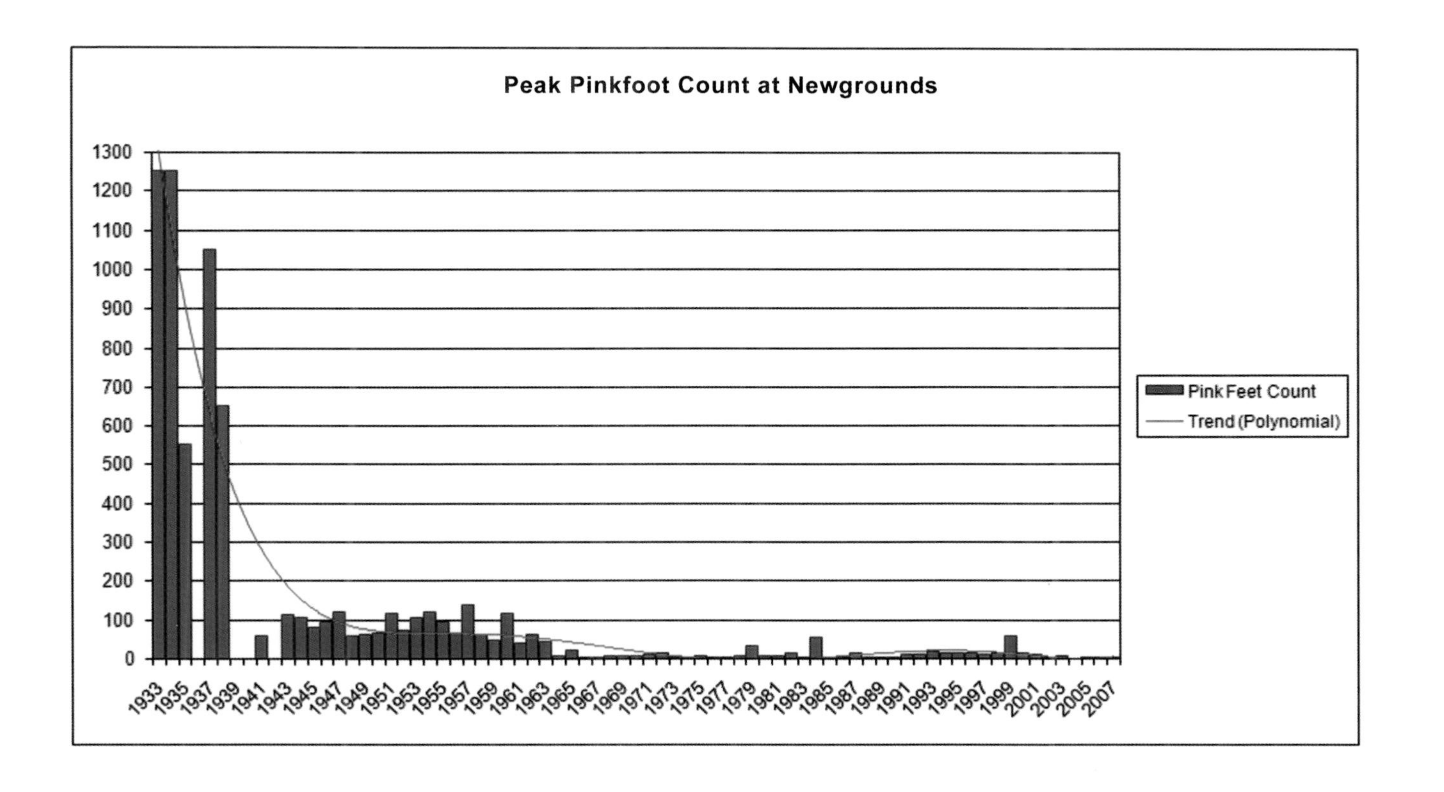
Peak Pinkfoot Count at Newgrounds
Pink Feet Count
Trend (Polynomial)
1300
1200
1100
1000
900
800
700
600
500
400
300
200
100
0
1933
1935
1937
1939
1941
1943
1945
1947
1949
1951
1953
1955
1957
1959
1961
1963
1965
1967
1969
1971
1973
1975
1977
1979
1981
1983
1985
1987
1989
1991
1993
1995
1997
1999
2001
2003
2005
2007

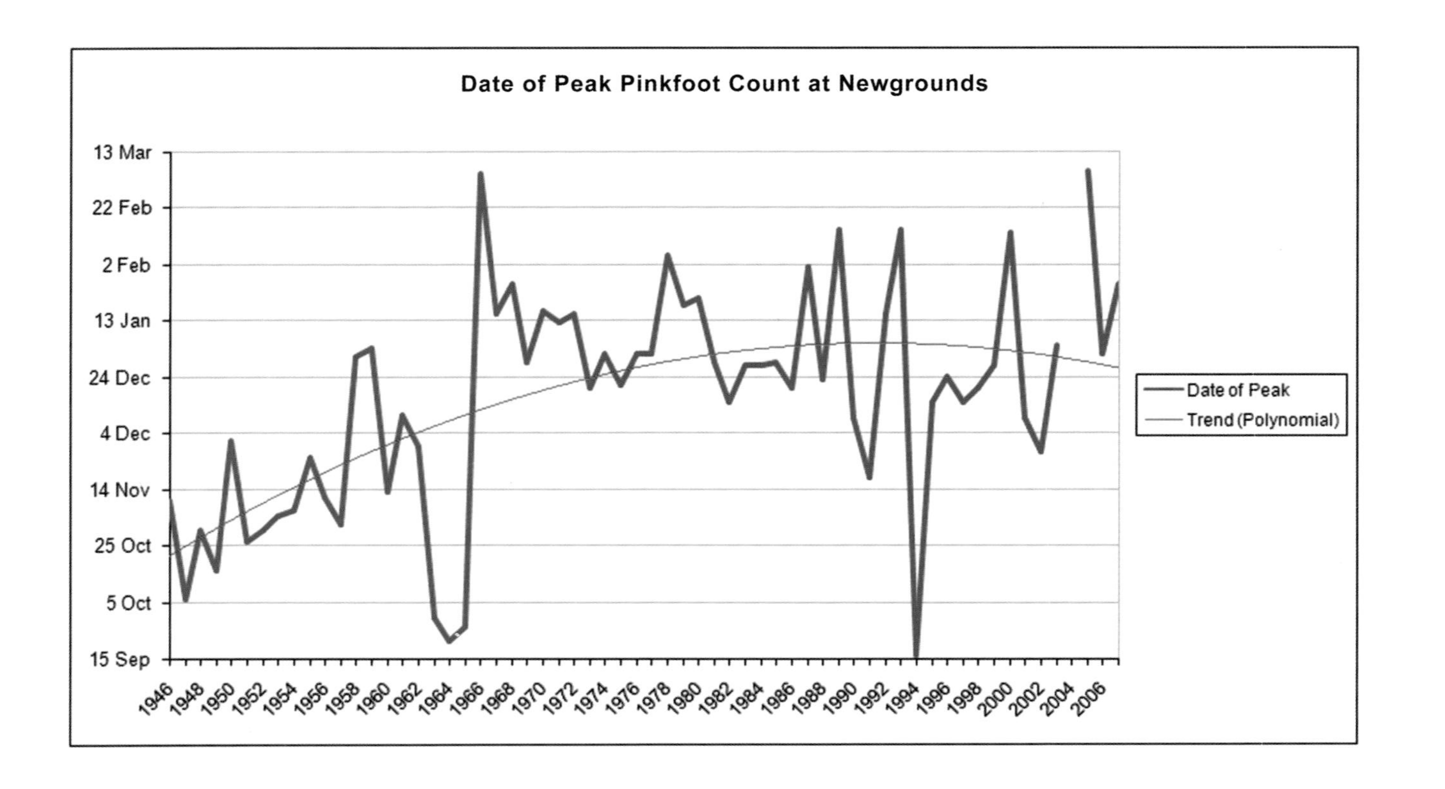

Date of Peak Pinkfoot Count at Newgrounds
13 Mar
22 Feb
2 Feb
13 Jan
24 Dec
4 Dec
14 Nov
25 Oct
5 Oct
15 Sep
1946
1948
1950
1952
1954
1956
1958
1960
1962
1964
1966
1968
1970
1972
1974
1976
1978
1980
1982
1984
1986
1988
1990
1992
1994
1996
1998
2000
2002
2004
2006
Date of Peak
Trend (Polynomial)

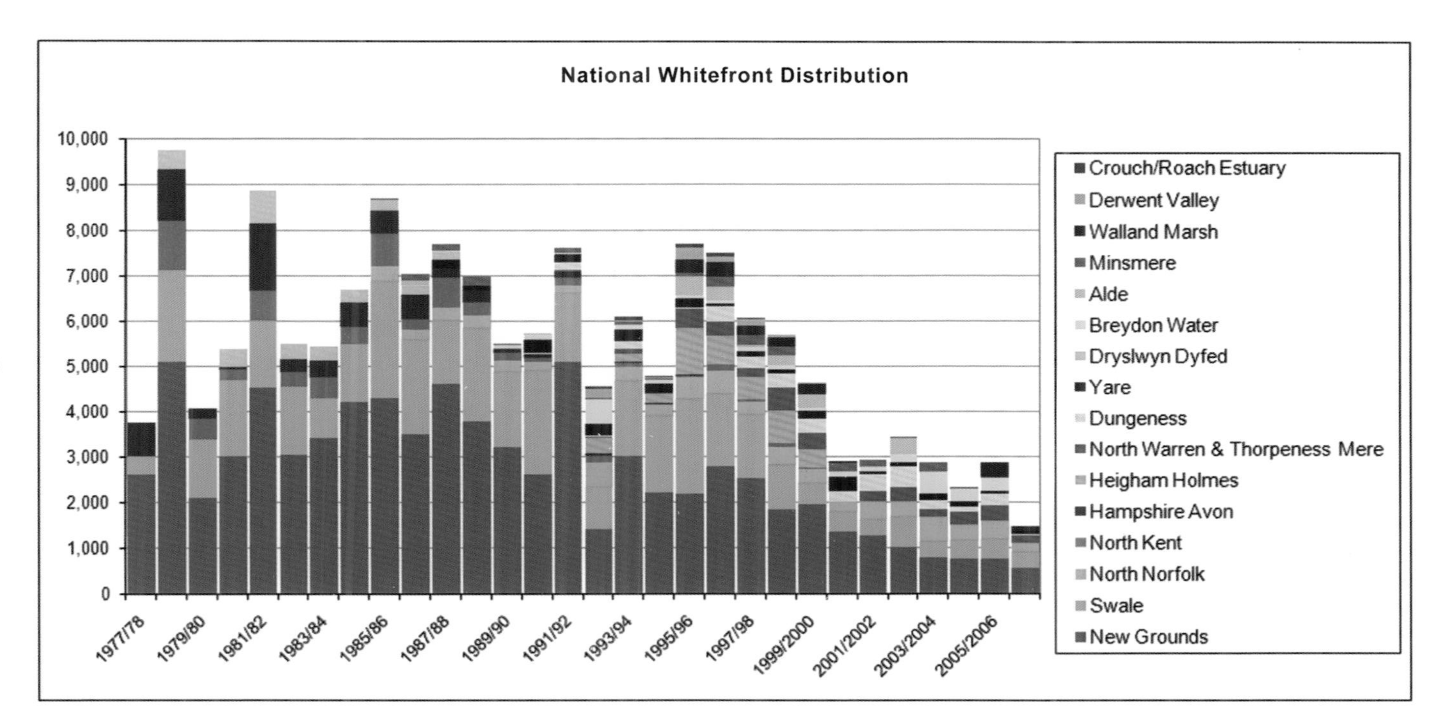
National Whitefront Distribution
10,000
9,000
8,000
7,000
6,000
5,000
4,000
3,000
2,000
1,000
0
1977/78
1979/80
1981/82
1983/84
1985/86
1987/88
1989/90
1991/92
1993/94
1995/96
1997/98
1999/2000
2001/2002
2003/2004
2005/2006
Crouch/Roach Estuary
Derwent Valley
Walland Marsh
Minsmere
Alde
Breydon Water
Dryslwyn Dyfed
Yare
Dungeness
North Warren & Thorpeness Mere
Heigham Holmes
Hampshire Avon
North Kent
North Norfolk
Swale
New Grounds

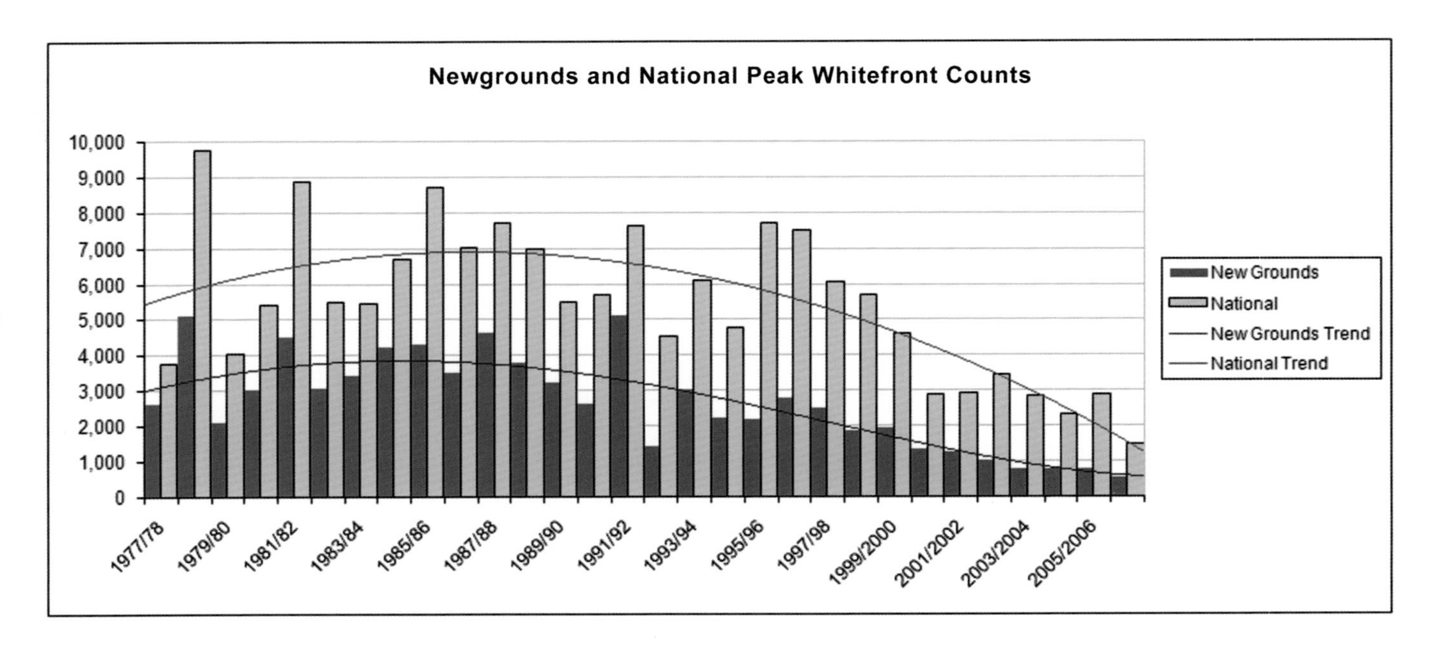

Newgrounds and National Peak Whitefront Counts
New Grounds
National
New Grounds Trend
National Trend
10,000
9,000
8,000
7,000
6,000
5,000
4,000
3,000
2,000
1,000
0
1977/78
1979/80
1981/82
1983/84
1985/86
1987/88
1989/90
1991/92
1993/94
1995/96
1997/98
1999/2000
2001/2002
2003/2004
2005/2006

Bibliography and works consulted

Morning Flight by Peter Scott. Country Life. 1935.

Wild Geese and Wild Duck Inquiry. International Wildfowl Enquiry by Dr John Berry. 2 volumes. Cambridge University Press. 1939.

The Frontier of a Barony by Francis Pitt. John Bellows. 1948.

Bulletin of the British Ornithologists Club. Vol. 68. No. 6. May, 1948.

Gloucestershire Stories. Hope Costley White. The British Publishing Co. 1949.

Wild Geese & Eskimos by Peter Scott. Country Life. 1951.

A Thousand Geese by Peter Scott & James Fisher. Collins. 1953.

Country Life Magazine. '*Catching Wild Geese with Rocket-nets*' by Peter Scott. September 29, 1955.

The Eye of the Wind by Peter Scott. Hodder & Stoughton. 1961.

Wildfowl in Great Britain. Monographs of the Nature Conservancy no. 3. Edited by George Atkinson-Willes. Published by Her Majesty's Stationery Office. 1963.

The Severn Bore by Fred Rowbotham. David & Charles. 1964.

Waterfowl by Peter Scott. Berkshire Printing Company. 1973.

Handbook to the Birds of Europe the Middle East and North Africa.
Stanley Cramp, Chief Ed. Volume 1. Oxford University Press. 1977.

Wild Geese by Malcolm A Ogilvie. T & A D Poyser. 1978.

Wild Geese of the World by Myrfyn Owen. Batsford Press. 1980.

Observations of Wildlife by Peter Scott. Phaidon. 1980.

Wildfowl in Great Britain. Second Edition. Myrfyn Owen, George Atkinson-Willes & David Salmon. Cambridge University Press. 1986.

A Coloured Key to the Wildfowl of the World by Peter Scott. Published by the Wildfowl Trust. Revised edition 1988.

The Severn Estuary. A Heritage of Wildlife. Severn Estuary Conservation Group. 1990.

Man & Wildfowl by Janet Kear. T & A D Poyser. 1990.

Wildfowl and Wader Counts. 1979-80 through to 1989-90. 11 copies. Published by the Wildfowl and Wetlands Trust under contract to the Nature Conservancy Council. David Salmon, Mike Moser, Jeff Kirby, R P Prys-Jones, R J Waters.

Ducks of the World by Janet Kear. Published by Charles Letts. 1991.

Peter Scott, Painter and Naturalist by Elspeth Huxley. Faber & Faber. 1993.

The Wildfowl & Wetlands Trust. Compiled by Diana Fowler & Simon Eckley. Chalford Publishing. 1996.

The Mighty Severn Bore by Chris Witts. River Severn Publications. 1999.

The Wetland Bird Survey. 1999-2000. *'Wildfowl & Wader Counts'.* A J Musgrove, M S Pollitt, C Hall, R D Hearn, S J Holloway, P E Marshall, J A Robinson, & P A Cranswick. 2001.

Disasters on the Severn by Chris Witts. Tempus Publishing Ltd. 2002.

The Wetland Bird Survey 2000-01. *'Wildfowl & Wader Counts'.* M S Pollitt, C Hall, S J Holloway, R D Hearn, P E Marshall, A J Musgrove, J A Robinson, & P A Cranswick. 2003.

The Wetland Bird Survey 2001-03. *'Wildfowl & Wader Counts'.* P A Cranswick, J Worden, R M Ward, H E Rowell, C Hall, A J Musgrove, R D Hearn, S J Holloway, A N Banks, G E Austin, L R Griffin, B Hughes, M Kershaw, M J O'Connell, M S Pollitt, E C Rees & L E Smith. 2005.

The Wetland Bird Survey 2003-04. *'Wildfowl & Wader Counts'*. M Collier, A Banks, G Austin, T Girling, R Hearn & A Musgrove. 2005.

Waterbirds in the UK 2004/05. A Banks, M Collier, G Austin, R Hearn & A Musgrove. 2006.

Gloucestershire Bird Reports. Editors include David Evans, Richard ffrench, Martin McGill, Rick Goater, Paul Marshall, Malcolm Ogilvie, John Sanders and C M Swaine, 1st to 44th report. 1963 to present copy.

Ducks, Geese and Swans by Janet Kear (Editor) Oxford University Press. 2 volume set. 2005.

Whitefronted Geese
Peter Scott

Glossary of Wetlands & Waterfowl

A.B.W.A.K.	Association of British Wild Animal Keepers.
A.E.W.A.	African-Eurasian Migratory Waterbird Agreement.
A.O.U.	American Ornithologists' Union.
Aberrant:	An abnormal, normally a species that is unlike the others in the group to which it is classified.
Algae:	The family of simple plants, such as the seaweeds.
Alula:	The 'bastard wing' thumb or first digit.
Anatatidae:	The family of birds that contains the swans, geese & ducks.
Anser:	The grey geese.
Anseriformes:	The order of birds that includes the Anatidae.
Aquatic:	Associated with water.
Arboreal:	To live in trees.
Axilla:	Wing; the arm pit.
B.A.S.C.	British Association for Shooting and Conservation. (Founded in 1908 as The Wildfowlers' Association of Great Britain and Ireland).
BL.I.	Birdlife International.
B.M.R.	Basic Metabolic Rate.
B.o.E.E.	Birds of Estuaries Enquiries.
B.O.U.	British Ornithologists' Union.
B.S.C.	Biological Species Concept.
B.T.O.	The British Trust for Ornithology.
Badelyng:	Collective noun of ducks.

Band:	Collective noun of plovers. (see also Congregation, Flight, Wing or Stand).
Black Geese:	A description to the darker geese, namely the Canada, Barnacle and Brent Geese.
Branta:	The black geese.
Brood:	The young hatched from a single clutch of eggs.
Bunch:	Collective noun of Teal or Wigeon (small number is referred to as a Little Knob).
C.I.T.E.S.	Convention on Trade in Endangered Species.
C.C.W.	Countryside Council for Wales.
C.W.S.	Canadian Wildlife Service.
Cere:	Bare fleshy area at base of bill, often coloured.
Clutch:	The number of eggs laid by a female before incubation starts.
Cob:	Male of swan.
Coil:	Collective noun of Teal. (see also Spring).
Colony:	Collective noun of gulls.
Company:	Collective noun of Wigeon.
Congregation:	Collective noun of Plovers. (see also flight, wing, band or stand).
Covert:	Collective noun of Coots.
Creche:	The young of many broods gathered together (for safety).
Cygnet:	Young of swan.
Deceit:	Collective noun of Lapwing.
Decoy: (1)	A pond of about one acre, out of which netted pipes radiate out, into which duck are lured by a dog. Traditionally they were killed for the market. Now ringed for scientific study. The W.W.T. run two.
Decoy: (2)	A plastic replica of a species of duck or goose, used by wildfowlers set out in a feeding pattern to appear as a group of duck on the water, to entice wild birds close enough to shoot. Traditionally these decoys were carved

from wood and painted. These are now highly collected as works of art and can be very valuable. Today's decoy carvers are highly specialised and produce them solely as works of art.

Decrescendo call: The call given by the female duck, the series of quacks going down in pitch and sound.

Desert: Collective noun of Lapwing.

Dimorphic: Different forms, often refers to the male and female in ducks (or birds) having different plumages.

Diurnal: To be active during daylight.

Dopping: Collective noun of Shelduck.

Down: Very soft under-feathers in wildfowl.

Drake: Male of duck.

E.N. English Nature.

E.S.A. Environmentally Sensitive Area.

Eclipse: The plumage change of drakes (male duck) takes on duller plumage of female, also flightless for a period.

Endemic: Within a defined area.

Equatorial: Within the tropical regions.

Estuarine: In an estuary, or where a river meets the sea.

Falcated: Sickle shaped.

Fall: Collective noun of Woodcock.

Flapper: A young duck.

Flight: Collective noun of Dunlin, Cormorant, Pochard or Plover.

Flock: Collective noun of geese on the water.

Flush: Collective noun of Mallards. (see also Sord & Sute)

Fulvous: Reddish-yellow or tawny.

G.C.T. Game Conservancy Trust Ltd.

Gaggle: Collective noun of geese on the ground.

Game: Collective noun of swans. (see also Herd or Wedge).

Gander: The male goose.

Grey Geese: Description of the lighter geese, namely the White-fronted, Bean, Pink-footed or Greylag Geese.

Gosling: Young of geese.

Herd: Collective noun of Swans, Curlews or Cranes.

Holarctic: The region north of the tropics including the Old & New Worlds.

Hybrid: Different species of birds producing an offspring. Once popular within collections of wildfowl, cross breeding.

I.B.A. Important Bird Area.

I.U.C.N. International Union for the Conservation of Nature and Natural Resources.

I.W.C. International Wildfowl Count.

I.W.R.B. International Waterfowl & Wetlands Research Bureau. (Now W.I.)

Immature: Non-adult.

Incubation: The sitting of a bird on a clutch of eggs producing heat.

Instinctive: To be born with inbuilt information.

J.N.C.C. Joint Nature Conservancy Committee.

Juvenile: Young bird, refers to a bird when it has got its first covering of feathers.

Lamella: Tooth like serrations on ducks' bills, used for sifting.

Mandibles: The upper and lower bills of birds.

Monomorphic: In one form, where plumage is the same in both sexes.

Moult: The losing of old feathers.

Moult Migration: A movement of birds prior to the wing-moult.

Muster: Collective noun of storks. (See also Mustering).

Mustering: Collective noun of storks. (See also Muster).

N.C.C. Nature Conservancy Council. (now defunct). See E.N., C.C.W & S.N.H.)

N.N.R. National Nature Reserve.

N.W.C. National Wildfowl Counts.

Nearctic: The arctic regions or North America or New World.

Nuptial: The Breeding Season.

Nuptial Plumage: The finery of the breeding plumage.

Old Squaw: Another name for the Long-Tail Duck.

Paddles: Wildfowls' webbed feet.

Paddling: Collective noun of ducks on the water.

Pair Bond: Long term pairing. (as in the swans & geese).

Palearctic: Arctic region of the Old World.

Palmipedes: Web-footed birds.

Pen: The female of swan.

Pin Feather: The new growing feather still in its sheath.

Piper: Traditional name of dog used in a decoy.

Plump: Collective noun of wildfowl. (see also Trip).

Primary Feathers: The outer wing feathers.

Pullus: A young bird, chick, prior to its first full plumage.

Quarry: The birds that may be hunted/taken legally by wildfowlers/hunters.

Quill: The strong, stiff feathers of a duck's wing and tail.

Quinck: The goose.

R.S.N.C. Royal Society for Nature Conservation.

R.S.P.B. The Royal Society for the Protection of Birds.

Raft: A tightly packed group of ducks on the water.

Ramsar Convention: An international conference held at Ramsar in Iran in 1971 which produced the Ramsar Convention whereby 'Countries recognised the interdependence of man and his environment' and undertook to protect their Wetlands of Importance.

Rush: Collective noun of Pochard. (see also Flight).

S.N.H.	Scottish Natural Heritage.
S.P.A.	Special Protection Area.
S.P.N.R.	Society for the Promotion of Nature Reserves.
S.S.S.I.	Site of Special Scientific Interest.
Sawbill:	Serrated-billed Wildfowl; eg; Goosander, Red-breasted Merganser and Smew.
Scapulars:	The feathers on the shoulders.
Seaduck:	Consists of the Scoter, Goldeneye, Merganser and Eider.
Sea Pheasant:	Another name for the Long-tail Duck.
Seasons:	The dates by which quarry species of geese and duck can be legally hunted. 1st September to 31st January extended to the 20th February where they are shot below mean high water.
Secondaries:	The inner flight feathers on the wing.
Siege:	Collective noun of herons or bitterns.
Summer Duck:	The Garganey.
Supercilium:	A stripe or marking above the eye.
Skein:	Collective noun of geese in flight.
Sord:	Collective noun of Mallards. (see also Flush or Sute).
Speculum:	The iridescent/bright secondary feathers on the wing of a duck.
Spring:	Collective noun of Teal. (see also Coil).
St Cuthbert's Duck:	Eider Duck.
Stand:	Collective noun of Plovers. (see also Congregation, Flight, Wing or Band.
Sute:	Collective noun of Mallards. (see also Flush or Sord).
Taiga:	The sub-arctic forest regions south of the Tundra.
Taxonomy:	The study of classification and evolutionary relationships.
Team:	Collective noun of ducks in flight.
Temperate regions:	The latitudes between the tropic lines and the polar circles.

Territory:	An area defended from all others.
Tertials:	The innermost secondary feathers.
Trachea:	The windpipe.
Trip:	Collective noun of wildfowl or Dotterel.
Tropical:	The areas within the Tropics of Cancer and Capricorn.
Tundra:	The arctic lands between the Taiga treeline and the northern permafrost.
Vasculation:	The supply of blood vessels to the skin area. (As in the wildfowls' paddles/feet).
Vermiculation:	The finely marked feathers on the breast of a duck, the Gadwall being a good example.
W.A.G.B.I.	The Wildfowlers' Association of Great Britain and Ireland. Now B.A.S.C. Founded in 1908 by Stanley Duncan.
WeBS:	Wetlands Bird Survey. Produces the Wildfowl & Waders Counts.
W.H.T.	The Wildlife Habitat Trust. Set up by B.A.S.C. members in 1986 as the members' conservation fund. Runs an annual habitat stamp programme to raise funds.
W.S.G.	Wader Study Group.
W.W.F.	World Wide Fund for Nature. (Formally The World Wildlife Fund).
W.W.T	The Wildfowl & Wetlands Trust. (originally Severn Wildfowl Trust, later Severn dropped)
W.I.	Wetlands International. (Formerly I.W.R.B.)
Walk:	Collective noun of Snipe at rest. (see also Wisp).
Waterfowl:	Water birds. Contains a large number of families. Those occurring in the U.K: divers, grebes, cormorants, herons, storks, Ibises and spoonbills, wildfowl, cranes, rails, waders and gulls and terns.
Wedge:	Collective noun of swans. (see also Herd or Game).
Whiffling:	Geese and ducks turning their bodies in flight to dispel air from under the wings to allow them to lose height quickly.

White Nun: Another name for the Smew.

Wildfowl: In Britain a term used for the swans, geese and ducks.

Wildfowler: A hunter who shoots on the foreshore, below the high water mark in the hope that a wild duck or goose may fly over his chosen spot.
Normally undertaken at dawn or dusk.

Wildfowling Season: 1st September to 31st January with an extension to 20th February when shooting below the high water mark.

Wing: Collective noun of plovers.
(see also Congregation, Flight, Band Or Stand.

Wisp: Collective noun of Snipe in flight. (see also Walk).

Winter Swans: The migratory swans; The Whooper or Bewick's Swan.

A Lesser Whitefront

Greenland White-fronted Geese

Sponsors' List

The Friends of Slimbridge and the author are enormously grateful to all sponsors who gave so generously towards this project.

Brigadier & Mrs S T Baldry
R J G Berkeley
John Bishop
Joe & Jan Blossom
Richard Chappell & Ennis Jones
Ray Ching
Martin Cook
Mr Aidan John Dryden
Helga & Bill Earle
Kath & Andy Edgeworth
Ralph & Daphne Ellis
Frampton Country Fair
Yvonne Harnden
Haydn & Sarah Jones
Gordon Kirk
Frank & Liz Lander
Sam Mackenzie
Graham & Wendy Maples
Martin McGill
Adrian Pound
Mr & Mrs Doug Radley
C B Rhys Jones in memory of Theo Rhys Jones
Dr M J Rogers
Lee Scragg
Severn Counties Foreign & British Bird Society
Bettie Sloane
John & Janie Sloane
Chris Temblett
Carmel & Alan Terry
Paul & Sue Walkden
Mo & Ron Warren
Diane & Peter Yeman

Subscribers' List

The Friends of Slimbridge and the author would like to thank the following who kindly supported this project.

Louise Adams
Simon Aldridge
Ken Atkinson & family
William Alexander
Nick & Sarah Bayston
Clifford R Bower
Jane & Mike Bridge
Mrs Joan Bryan
David, Helen & Olivia Chaffe
Paul & Sue Daunter
John & Trish Dryden
Norman Ellinson
Jeanne & John Fawcett
Robert Gillmor
Jim Greatrix
Anna Hall
Peter Hogan
Jack Jackson
Nigel Jarrett
Tony & Yvonne Johnson
Barbara Joy
Barbara & Peter Kerby
Tony Laws
Howard Lloyd
Daniel Lord & Sarah Munoz-Echeverria
Miss J E Maples
Robin & Pam Marshall-Ball
Brenda Moatt
Pam Morley
R M Ormrod
Jenny Ovens
Margaret Overton
Bruce Pearson
Michael Robinson
Tanya Rome
Angela & David Rosser
Tony Rye
Derek & Ann Sanders
P W Scragg
Pam Scroop
Edwin Shackleton
Roy Slade
Alan Smith
Beryl Smith
Sam Smith
Harry Temblett
Kevin W Tudor
Mr G E O Tudor
June Watkins
B M Wilden

The Wildfowl and Wetlands Trust

The Wildfowl & Wetlands Trust (WWT) is a leading UK conservation organisation saving wetlands for wildlife and people across the world.

WWT's nine visitor centres in the UK give one million visitors each year opportunities to get close to wetland wildlife and become actively involved in conservation.

WWT exists to save wetlands and their wildlife and raise awareness of the issues that affect their survival. And to enrich people's lives through learning about and being close to nature and inspiring them to help WWT's conservation work worldwide.

"What WWT has achieved matches Sir Peter Scott's ambition for it and is an astonishing achievement." Sir David Attenborough

As the UK's leading wetland conservation charity, we rely on the support and generosity of individuals, trusts and companies to achieve our goals. You can help in lots of ways:

- Join WWT as a member
- Support our latest appeal
- Become a WWT Patron
- Make a donation
- Volunteer your time
- Adopt a bird for yourself or a friend
- Remember WWT in your will

For more information please call 01453 891900 or visit www.wwt.org.uk

WWT's wetland centres cover 2,000 hectares of land and every centre is different.

WWT Arundel Wetland Centre, Mill Road, Arundel, West Sussex BN18 9PB, 01903 883355 www.wwt.org.uk/arundel

WWT Caerlaverock Wetland Centre, Eastpark Farm, Caerlaverock, Dumfriesshire DG1 4RS, 01387 770200 www.wwt.org.uk/caerlaverock

WWT Castle Espie Wetland Centre, 78 Ballydrain Road, Comber, Co Down BS23 6EA, 028 9187 4146 www.wwt.org.uk/castleespie

WWT London Wetland Centre, Queen Elizabeth's Walk, London SW13 9WT, 020 8409 4400 www.wwt.org.uk/london

WWT Martin Mere Wetland Centre, Burscough, Ormskirk, Lancashire L40 0TA, 01704 895181 www.wwt.org.uk/martinmere

WWT National Wetland Centre Wales, Llwynhendy, Llanelli, Carmarthenshire SA14 9SH, 01554 741087 www.wwt.org.uk/llanelli

WWT Slimbridge Wetland Centre, Slimbridge, Gloucestershire GL2 7BT, 01453 891900 www.wwt.org.uk/slimbridge

WWT Washington Wetland Centre, Pattinson, Washington, Tyne & Wear NE38 8LE, 0191 416 5454 www.wwt.org.uk/washington

WWT Welney, Hundred Foot Bank, Welney, Nr Wishbech, Cambridgeshire PE14 9TN 01353 860711 www.wwt.org.uk/welney